*Vincent Teresa*

# WISEGUYS

PANTHER
**GRANADA PUBLISHING**
London Toronto Sydney New York

Published by Granada Publishing Limited
in Panther Books 1979

ISBN 0 586 04867 7

A Panther UK Original
Copyright © Vincent Teresa 1978

Granada Publishing Limited
Frogmore, St. Albans, Herts AL2 2NF
and
3 Upper James Street, London W1R 4BP
1221 Avenue of the Americas, New York, NY 10020, USA
117 York Street, Sydney, NSW 2000, Australia
100 Skyway Avenue, Toronto, Ontario, Canada M9W 3A6
110 Northpark Centre, 2193 Johannesburg, South Africa
CML Centre, Queen & Wyndham, Auckland 1, New Zealand

Made and printed in Great Britain by
Cox & Wyman Ltd, London, Reading and Fakenham
Set in Intertype Baskerville

# CHAPTER ONE

We been here three nights now at this particular motel, me and these marshals, and for three nights I've won anywhere from fifty to seventy-five dollars, which is a lot of money in this small card game. They haven't got a chance. I mean, if I really put my mind to it, it's like taking candy from a baby. They don't know; they're chasers trying to fill an inside straight. Real sucker moves. And it's not that I'm cheating; it's just smarter card-playing. If I couldn't beat these clowns, I couldn't beat anybody. Meantime, *they're* the ones that's sitting with the guns strapped to them. They look like Wyatt Earp. I'm waiting any minute for someone to say, 'Reach for it, partner, you're cheating!'

You see, what it is, they're not concentrating. I mean, they're acting like they're not scared, but there's no question about it, they're scared out of their heads. They know they're not fooling around with small-timers. Like why don't somebody open up a window or why don't someone open up one of these big sliding glass doors and let some fresh air in? I know why they won't. They're scared that somebody will take a pop at me. And they're right.

I'm sitting here sweating, and it's going back through my mind the time that a couple of old friends of mine – Nick and Tony – were sitting at a card table in a room less than a quarter of a mile away from here, in another broken-down joint. I remember Butch and I, we knew where these two guys were, and the Old Man said, 'They're doing the wrong thing, go and get them.' They were playing poker with four other guys, shills that were on our payroll, who were there to set up these two

5

dangerous monkeys. Butch and I went there, and one of our men opened the door. We went in with sawed-off shotguns. Our men knew what was coming; they fell to the floor and when they did we opened up. It was a mob-protected joint and no one paid no attention. A couple of guests made complaints, I understand later, but it didn't do a bit of good. Said it was someone backfiring. And Nick and Tony were taken out of the room and put in the trunk of a car and left there. Car stood there for seven days until it stunk. That's how it was finally discovered ...

I don't jump out of my skin when the phone rings, but I strain to hear what's being said. I mean, I'm very much on edge. Because you can't imagine the thoughts that go through your head, just sitting around here all day. Like you say to yourself, Is this a setup? If it ain't a setup how stupid can they be? We're in an area here where guys get killed every night for nothing, never mind for something. All kinds of things go on in these crummy motels.

It could be a phone call from them – the guys who are after me. If it is from them, it's a setup, and right now they're telling the marshal, 'Okay, do it now.'

The marshal talks for a couple of minutes, very low, and I say, 'Was that Mister Oakes?'

'No,' he says. No explanation.

'Was there any problem?'

'No problem.'

I feel like saying, 'Was that your wife on the phone, your girl? Who the hell was it and what the hell's going on? I mean, is there something I should know about? After all, it's my life.' But you can't get no answers out of them. They're instructed by headquarters in Washington not to say anything to anybody.

Then I hear a couple of guys talking outside the door and I take a few deep breaths. Am I going to get it now? I look around the room fast. What can I grab to protect myself with? What can I get behind? Can I grab a gun off one of these jerks? My heart is pounding and I feel a little dizzy. I got to get away from these people, got to walk around a little bit. I throw my cards down.

'Look, cash me in,' I say. 'I can't play no more.'

And one guy gives me an argument. 'Hey, geez, I'm stuck about fifteen bucks. You going to leave me?'

'You're stuck fifteen dollars!' I say. 'I'm worried about being whacked out and you're worried about fifteen rotten dollars!' And George, one of the older marshals, the one that was almost asleep, speaks up. 'Look, if he don't want to play, he don't have to play.' Because it would just take me about three minutes to have a damn good fight with this guy and take out my aggravations on him. It's really a bad situation when some clown looks up at you and says, 'Hey, you can't leave because I'm stuck for fifteen dollars.' That shows me where his concern for my life is. I'm not scared, I'm nervous. There's a difference between being scared and nervous. I'm nervous because I don't think these jerks know their job. I don't believe that I'm going to get away with this. So the card game breaks up and I hear the loser over in the corner saying, 'Son-of-a-bitch! Mister Johnny Forza beat me for fifteen dollars and quit. Is that the way they do it on the street?'

I throw the dollar bills at him. 'You miserable bastard! Keep your money! Who the hell wants it, you sucker? I could beat you every day in the week. You think I need your rotten fifteen dollars? Here!'

And I go next door to my room and I sit on the edge of my bed. I'm just sitting there saying to myself, 'Boy, I wish I could get at this phone and call Nancy.' Talking to her would at least relax my mind a little. It's getting to me, not being able to call her, not being able to call anybody. I know the mob has got me bugged – my mother's phone, Nancy's phone, my sister's, and everybody else. So it's ridiculous. I wouldn't even mind talking to Carla. Not that we get along at all. We don't. Who gets along with his

7

wife? But it'd be a voice at least that I know. They don't have her phone covered because they don't know where she is, but I can't even call her. Suppose they got this motel wired? Or they got a guy down on the desk that lets them know the number I called? Either way they find where the government relocated us, and they're waiting for me when I get back there. So I can't call nobody. And tonight is just one of those nights that I feel like a mosquito on the wall. I'm so jittery I'm dancing all over the place and I don't know what to do with myself. I'd like to grab one of these turkeys' guns and go in there and blast them all and run out in the middle of the street and yell, 'Now, you bastards, come get me!'

I get up and start walking around. I don't know what to do with myself, and tomorrow I've got to go in and face them in a trial. Already my mouth is starting to get dry just thinking about it. Because this is going against everything I knew all my life. When I close my eyes I can hear the Old Man saying, 'He is my son, he is my blood ...' And when he sent me the word of silence, I knew he'd kill me just to keep the Society powerful. Not to obey that word is disaster, and from then on my life wasn't worth two cents.

I'm walking back and forth in this room and I look at this goddamn bed and the mattress has got a swayback like a horse. It's an old broken-down joint, you know. They never take you to a half-decent, plush place because they can't afford it, but they give you the excuse I might run into some guy I knew off the street, and none of them would be staying in a fleabag like this. If they had any brains these marshals would go right to the best place around the corner from where the nightclubs are. Maybe the mob won't even think of looking there.

You know, I suggested to the marshals that they drive Cadillacs when they got me. Because Butch and his people won't be looking for Cadillacs. They'll be looking for a government car. Beat-up, plain, hardly any chrome. Black tires. Sticks out like a sore thumb. Oh, but no sir, the government people have always got to economize and they're economizing on me. They don't think, these guys. To save a couple of dollars on their expense sheets they go to the desk clerk when we check in and say, 'We're United States Marshals, we'd like a government commercial rate.' Big thing, they save two or three dollars and they put my life in danger. Any jerk could find me.

Butch knows I got to be somewhere near the courthouse, like no more than an hour's drive. So how many hotels and motels does he have to check? Not as many as you think. He knows I won't be in a midtown Manhattan joint and he knows the marshals prefer motels cause they're cheaper and easy to get in and out of without being seen. That leaves the motels out of Manhattan – maybe two, three dozen places and Butch can narrow it down easy. First, he figures the obvious place is an airport motel, since it'd be easier to get me in and out of New York – too easy. So he crosses that one off. A lot of them are mob-connected anyway. What does that leave? Well, not too many places. There's a bunch of motels the other side of the Lincoln Tunnel and then one here and there in Brooklyn, Queens, Nassau. And we're staying in one of those here-and-there places right in the middle of Queens. A hot-bed joint where salesmen bring receptionists during lunch hour. So all he does is check till he finds the motel with the gang of United States Marshals staying in it, with all the activity of people being so secretive. Don't allow no maid in the room. Bring my meals up from the restaurant. You think that goes without notice? We're in exactly the kind of place Butch will figure we'd stay in, and I'm sure he's got to have found us by now. I also know that he'll figure I know this and will be expecting him, but he knows I can't do nothing about it, that I don't give the orders here.

You wonder how I figure my old pal, Butch, is the one that's after me? Couldn't be anybody else. The Old Man has to whack a guy out, he sends a guy who knows him – his best friend, a guy the guy trusts. If you're after a guy on the lam you put a guy in charge who knows the lamster like a book – where he's going to go, what he's going to do. And Butch fits that description perfect. If the Old Man didn't give him the action, he asked for it. I don't mean Butch is going to do the hit himself. He might, but he's more than likely to be the brains behind the job, the guy that plans it and then sends out the mechanics to get it done.

Look around this dirty room. Look at that clown over in the corner, he's half asleep. The other guy's watching television. These guys are incredible jerks. Don't they see there's no escape out of here? No way out in the back. There's one door and that's the end of it. I feel as though any minute the whole place is going to blow up. I hear a car coming. Is it someone to hurt me? Maybe just some guys that want to get laid. I'm trying to be quiet. I'm trying not to let them know my nerves are tingling, because if this is a setup, let Butch think I'm cool and maybe he'll be scared to make a move against me. If he knows I'm breaking up he's going to make a move that much faster.

I got no chances at all. If Butch and his men ever decide to come in they'd take out these marshals fast. Somebody'd just kick that door in. For chrissake, by the time a marshal found a gun, they'd be two days into a wake. Or maybe Butch would have them send up a waitress. She'd knock on the door and, 'I have coffee for you people. It was sent up by the office.' And one of these jerks, to get a free cup of coffee, would open the door and that's that. Once they open that door, two, three guys jump in, and you think they're just going to hit me? They hit everybody in the place. Level it. Blast it. You understand?

I know if I was doing this, I'd survey the area and if it

didn't look as though they had outside arms – guards hiding in the trees – I would get together three, four cowboys and wait until I thought the least people would be in there, and I'd come and knock on the door. I'd storm the joint, because mob guys know about marshals. They know they're not sitting around with guns across their laps. They know they're very lax people. There should be a man outside the door and a man down in the front in a car checking in every five minutes with a walkie-talkie, finding out if everything is okay or not. And someone on the roof watching things coming and going. Will Butch storm the joint here? I think he won't because that's what he knows I expect and he'll figure I got to warn the marshals to be ready. He can't be sure if they listen to me, but he's going to do something more clever, sneaky – the kind of thing I won't expect out of him. Knows it'll make me sweat more than an attack. Maybe he poisons my food.

I'm saying to myself, 'Why are you really worrying? You're going to get yours eventually. Just pray. Hope and pray that they hit you at the base of the skull so you go out immediately, no suffering. You're ten times better off than if you died of cancer, after being a vegetable the last ten years of your life.' I don't want none of that. I enjoyed living up until now, now I want to enjoy dying. But don't torture me. I don't want to be walking down the street and then all of a sudden two guys grab me and throw me in the car. I know they're going to do things to me like cut my joint off and stick it in my mouth, get a dead sparrow and put it on my forehead, dump me in front of the police station like that.

Or they'll do to me what Vito the Butcher liked to do. I can't remember his last name. Well, there was a guy named Phil that opened up in the can on Vito that he was smuggling in some dope. When Vito got out he waited for Phil to get out and they found Phil down on the beach just completely torn apart, his arms twenty-five feet away from his chest and his head someplace else. And another guy, Rocky Ruggerio, done similar things, too – cut legs off and threw them. One time Rocky had a guy that'd been holding out. Rocky was trying to find where he kept the stash, and the guy was a tough nut. So Rocky took him out to a meat-packing plant one night and they hung the guy up on a meat hook and worked on him with one of them cattle prods, the kind that gives you a jolt of electricity. And he talked and then they finished him off. Cut him up with a power saw.

Or like the time they put away Mike and Big Al, another pair of pigeons. They took a wire and tied it around their balls and cut them off that way, then they took them and stuck them in their mouths, and they tied their throats so that their eyes were bulging out like bullfrogs. Made a grotesque situation, and they threw them in the river. There were no lead weights to them or cement or nothing; they knew they would be washed up along the shore where somebody would discover them with their bodies all puffed up.

This is what happens to all stool pigeons, you see. They're going to make an example of me. They're going to dissect me, throw a piece to the rats, throw a piece to the fish, leave just enough of me so that when the authorities find me they say, 'Hey, this is Johnny Forza, or what's left of him.' And it's going to get in the newspapers what happened, and from then on anybody else in the area's going to say, 'You want me to talk? What are you, crazy? Look what happened to Johnny Forza. And he was protected by the government? Take the government, who needs them! They let this guy get it like this? Bad enough you get killed, anybody can be killed, but to be taken apart, piece by piece like a Tinkertoy, no sir, don't want no part of you people. I'll stick with the mob, as bad as they are.'

You know, I keep thinking of Abe Reles getting pushed

out a hotel window with six cops guarding him night and day and they all had excuses. And I think about other people that were up tight with the mob and went with the government or the city and accidentally took a header or got shot in the back trying to escape and such things. If I get fresh with these marshals, one of them just might shove me over the balcony himself. I got a little news for you. I think if it wasn't for Mister Oakes I might have been shoved over a long time ago. I don't trust them. But I'm getting a little crazy in the head here and I got to be careful not to do the dumb thing. One of these marshals looks at me funny and I want to shank him.

So I start walking around the room and my mouth is all dry and I'm all sweaty and I decide I'm going to take a shower. It's a rotten warm night inside the motel, muggy from all the people in this room. And then I hear somebody walking up the stairs to the second floor and I say, 'Now, who the hell can this be?' I hear a knock on the door of the other room and then I hear Mister Oakes's voice, thank God. And he comes in and says, 'How's Johnny?'

'Oh, I guess he's okay.'

'What do you mean, "you guess"? When was the last time you looked?' He's talking to the marshals. I hear him walking towards my door and I yell, 'I'm okay, Mister Oakes. I'm fine. Don't worry about it.'

'They're treating you all right?' he asks.

'Oh, yeah. Terrific.' I ain't about to complain to him. I'm not looking for these guys to lose their jobs. It ain't going to do me any good, it ain't going to make them any smarter, if I complain.

I call Mister Oakes 'Mister' because I respect him. I feel as though any man that is laying his life on the line as much as he is, and is the only fair guy I've really bumped-ed into in the whole United States Marshals, deserves to be called Mister. Many a time Mister Oakes has told me to call him by his first name, but it's like I just couldn't bring myself to do it. He's not that much older than me, but he's taken a chance to be respectful towards me, and I have to show my respect. He's taken a chance because most federal people think guys like me are dirt to be stepped on. Mister Oakes is all for the Witness Protection Program, and the rest of them give him the business over it. Every time he tries to make a move to help a witness, he gets the worst of it. They even say that he's holding hands with us, taking bribes and stuff like that, which is a lot of bullshit.

Mister Oakes comes in and sits down across the bed from me. He looks like an ex-fullback for the Giants – you know, big-boned, rough-faced, Irish-looking guy. I think he used to be a state cop somewhere in New England. Mister Oakes is the only man here that's worth his salt, the only one I can think of that if a real emergency comes up he will be able to hack it. If you want to be corny about it, I can relate to this guy because he looks like he belongs on the street. And he's smiling at me and saying, 'Come on now, John. Take it easy. What the hell you worried about? You have no confidence in me?'

'Yes, Mister Oakes, I got a lot of confidence in you, but the rest of these fools that you got here . . .'

'John,' he says, 'I'll keep them in line. Don't worry about it. Nothing's going to happen to you. Play the game the way I asked you to play it. And believe me,' he says, 'I'm worried about me as much as I am you.' And I'm saying to myself, 'You better worry, because when they come looking, if you're in the way they'll just as soon whack you and then get to me.'

'Let's go back and play some cards,' he says.

'Mister Oakes,' I say, 'I can't stand any more. I can't stand those guys' disconcern. You're the only one in the joint that is worried whether or not I'm going to make it. It's every man for himself, Mister Oakes,' I say. 'If some-

14

one busts into this room, I'm going to try for a gun,' I says, 'yours or anybody else's.'

'Take it easy, Johnny,' he says. 'I want you to leave this door open from now on.' And he walks out.

You know, when I first met this guy I wasn't too fond of him, but I wasn't too fond of anybody at that particular time. It was when they let me out of the joint after I said I'd testify against the mob and I was turned over to this Mister Oakes by the FBI who had been working the case. And the FBI says, 'We'll want to talk to him later on,' and Mister Oakes says, 'Well, I'm going to be staying at the Sheraton Hotel. I'll be in room such-and-such, if you want to see us.' In the meantime, no sooner did the FBI walk away than he turns around and says to the two men he's with, 'Come on. Get the hell out of here. Pack the clothes.' And we don't go to the Sheraton, we go to another hotel. And my feet are sweating. I say to myself, 'Well, maybe this guy's going to whack me out.' Who the hell knows of this guy? He didn't show up when the FBI wanted to talk to him. So, to find out, I question Mister Oakes, and he says to me, 'Listen, when you're in my charge, I don't want anybody to know where you are, including the FBI. Including my boss. Including everybody.' He says, 'The only ones know where you are, are the people right here this minute. The FBI wants me or you, they have to call my headquarters in Washington and they will make a call to a certain phone which will reach me.' This guy was smart enough not to trust any other cops at all, even though he was sort of a cop, you know. The marshals can't make an arrest but when Uncle Sam wants somebody guarded, they don't call the cops – they send in the marshals. Anyway, Oakes didn't trust nobody and that started to impress me.

I need some air, so I walk toward the sliding glass doors and – I got to stick my head – I'm going to look out and

15

. . . 'Hey! Get away from that goddamn door! What are you, crazy? You want to get shot?' It's one of the marshals yelling. And I pull back, saying to myself, 'You son-of-a-bitch! Who the hell you think you're talking to?' But I shouldn't knock. I don't think they're smart and I think they're in it just for the pensions, but they are here, and if someone starts shooting they're going to shoot back. They're not looking to protect me, they're looking to protect themselves. That could be good or bad. If I'm in the line of fire they'll say, 'Let him have it.' If I ain't in the line of fire they'll protect me, because they might be getting it themselves.

These marshals are all rough, knockabout guys, and outside of Tom – I mean Mister Oakes – are average size, you know. And they're dressed shabby. They got a pair of cheap pants on and a three-dollar white short-sleeved shirt that I would have wiped my car off with. And they love their damn beer, maybe because it's cheap. I know for supper (they give me fifteen dollars a day to eat with) I had them bring me in some nice roast beef, potatoes, and so forth, and I sat down to a hot meal. Not the marshals. They went to Kentucky Fried Chicken and came back with a dollar nineteen box, and the rest of the money they put in their pocket. That's why they're on the street and I'm in jail. They're willing to satisfy themselves with a dollar nineteen piece of chicken and not a nine-dollar piece of roast beef. There's the difference. I look for too much in life. They're satisfied with what's given them.

My God! How did I get into this? Son-of-a-bitch Butch! I just can't describe how bad I want him here in this room with me right now so I could take him and mangle his goddamn face and his head, the treacherous, devious bastard that he is. All my life I was on the alert for people like this. It could never have happened to me from anyone that wasn't close to me, because I was too smart and too clever and too suspicious. Anyone that wasn't close to me could never have got the advantage on me like Butch did.

I first met Butch hanging around the block. I seen this little kid playing pitch – throwing nickels and dimes and quarters up against a wall. He looked three or four years younger than me and was playing with older guys. That's what attracted my attention to him. Skinny kid, don't look as though he could have brushed a fly off his shoulder, and here he is playing around with kids that are four, maybe five years older than him. And the funny part about it, he's hustling them, pitching with a heavier coin which gives him an edge. He's jumping around like a donkey, and every time he pitches a coin he says, 'Hey, let me look and see how close it came.' He'd run up there and he'd nudge his coin, you see. So, they thought they were laughing at this jerky kid and meantime he'd end up with all the money.

It showed me two things about Butch. One, he was smart enough to play with guys that wouldn't think he'd try to get away with these things, guys that'd break his head. And two, he had balls enough to play with these guys, you understand? He could have played with younger kids or even kids his own age and beat them. But it wouldn't have been a challenge to him This guy always wanted to try and take someone down off his perch.

Butch was a born hustler. I was fifteen and he was twelve when his family moved into the neighborhood. I'd started out on the street corners shining shoes and now I was hustling crap games and doing a little breaking-and-entry on the side. For a kid my age, I always had a pretty good package of money on me, and Butch would always be trying to get up along side of me all the time. He'd say, 'Take me with you,' and 'Let me help you out, I'll do this and that . . .'

When you're a stickboy hustling, you're just like the guy who handles a dice table except you're on your hands and knees picking up the dice and they don't say they're going to pay you anything, but they give you a few. Not only that, but if a guy gets on a hot run he'd say, 'cool them off', and I'd blow on the dice for him and pick them up and roll them and shake them in my hand and love them and so forth. The guy gets lucky and he makes a score and, 'Here you are, kid, here's five dollars. Here's ten dollars.' I'll tell you the truth, I seen days when I made – Christ, I was thirteen, fourteen years old – on a Sunday, I made over a hundred dollars being a stickboy.

Anyway, what took place was that Butch became a finger man. I mean, his father, Carmine Lombardi, was a dealer in one of the mob card games, and he would hear his father telling his mother where he'd be working and Butch would pass this information to me. By this time I'm running with some older guys – seventeen- and eighteen- and nineteen-year-old fellas – and Butch would say, 'There's a crap game or a card game at such-and-such an address in Manhattan or in Brooklyn,' and we'd knock over the game, you know? Just bust in, line them up against the wall, and pick up all the money. And Butch would get a ten-percent cut.

Butch was always treacherous. Very, very shrewd and very treacherous. He was taking advantage of his family. He knew that we were going into crap games and card games where his father was dealing, and with guns, and it was very serious. Which could have meant that his father would get popped, but he didn't care. He hated his old man. I didn't like that in Butch.

Eventually, I got called in by some of the wildmen that ran these games, and I was told : 'Listen, you know you're doing wrong?'

I said, naturally, 'No, I don't know I'm doing wrong. Am I doing wrong?'

'Yes, you're not supposed to be holding up these games. They're protected by us, and what's going to happen is you're not going to be able to get in any more card games because people will be afraid to go to them because people like you are interpreting our services. And if you're a good boy and you stop, we'll try and help you earn a living in other ways. If you're not a good boy, we'll shoot you.'

And that would be that. Now this is one of the first times that I seen Butch show a lot of courage in the face of danger. He knew I was going in there to talk to those men and that they were going to give me a hard time. So he got at the edge of the door with a sawed-off shotgun – God knows where he got it – and yelled in : 'Listen, you greasers, if my friend Johnny isn't out of there in one piece right away I'm shooting anybody that tries to come through that door.'

And there he was, this skinny kid not fourteen years old, warning some of the meanest guys in the country to take it easy on his pal – and he got away with it. That's when I knew how close a bond was developed between him and I. From then on, as far as I was concerned, Butch was an equal partner, not a ten-percenter anymore. Whatever I made he got a piece of   I mean, when I made it through him. And there were a lot of scores that he set up, things like a load of furs that he heard his father talking about and helped us rob. He wasn't called Butch in those days. His real name is Frank Anthony Lombardi and he answered to Frankie, but he didn't like the sound of it. He liked to be called Butch because it made him sound tough, and he'd tell guys to call him that and sometimes they'd laugh. There's very few now who remember he was ever called anything else.

He had a lot of guts and a lot of brains and was very shrewd, and the thing was, he never forgot anything. If you told him something once it was like it was branded on his skull. He wasn't a *gabodosta,* he was smart. You could see that Butch was going to be a comer. He was the type of guy that not only learned what you taught him but he took advantage of it all the way down the line. Because after that incident with the mob, they told me they were going to let me earn some money and they did. They put me onto some hijackings, liquor and cigarettes and stuff like that – the whole trailer. I was going to work with some older professional people, and every time I was supposed to meet them and do things, Butch would make it his business to get involved with me so that I would have to take him along. But I wanted to because Butch was a good friend.

As we got older, Butch wasn't a skinny kid no more. He's a couple of inches taller than me and I'm five-ten, but I outweigh him by maybe twenty pounds. He's turned into a good-looking guy, black hair combed straight back, some pockmarks on his face, but a very, very fancy dresser, always with a white shirt and gray necktie no matter how hot it is. Never seen him in sports clothes. And he is so clean about himself; he showers every time he turns around and changes his clothes a couple of times a day. We used to go together to the barbershop at the Waldorf and get it all – just lay back and get a shave and a hair trim and manicure and shine. And we'd talk without mentioning names and I felt very close to Butch. I liked him.

And because I liked him I let my guard down, and look what happened to me. Look at me. I'm sitting in this room with these turkeys and my life is on the line – sitting here waiting to put my head in the lion's mouth by going into court. When I think of walking in front of them animals again, sitting on top of that stand and having them stare me down, I'm going to want to jump off the damn stand and run.

My mind is telling me, 'Don't go into that court. Don't do it.' I know in my heart that they will never forgive me whether I go in there or I don't, because I've already

20

gone before the grand jury and the damage is done. I know that they all done the wrong thing to me, and they did it first, and there's nothing that will ever change that, and now I got to get even with them. I can't get out in the street to do it. I'd love to make a run for it and see if I could get Butch, and then I wouldn't care what happened to me. Because I got this poison inside of me that drives me berserk every time I think that these son-of-a-bitches are on the street even though I'm taking them to trial. And with the money and power and political connections that's behind them, even if they get convicted they're still going to walk the streets again pretty soon. I know this.

Am I doing right? Deep down in my heart I know I'm not. This ain't the way you play the game. But what else can I do? I mean, is there any other way I can get back at this bastard, Butch? Or the Old Man? That one, the Old Man, he never should have broke his word to me. I never broke my word to him. He asked me to hit guys. I hit them. He asked me to beat up guys. I beat them up. He asked me to turn in my money. I turned my money in. Whatever he asked me to do, the Old Man, I done it. And Butch had no right crossing me. I never done nothing wrong to him unless he deserved it. I slapped him around once because he had it coming. I never beat him for his money. Whatever money we had coming, share and share alike. Why did he do this to me? Why? Why? Why? Why did this son-of-a-bitch do it to me? I'm sitting here smoking butts by the damn pack and thinking of all these things.

One time, when Butch and I were holding up a jewelry store, he was watching my back and saw a guard coming in the wrong door. We didn't expect him to come in, and Butch pops him, hits him in the leg. The guy goes to the ground and Butch saves my life. So I owe him. And when you owe someone on the street you always pay, you're

obligated to pay. A year later, I'm going to see the grease-
ball one day, Mister Scordato, and he says, 'Boys, I got a
job for you, a real good job.' He says, 'I been watching
you for a long time now and I think it's time that we're
gonna give you a very important assignment. We have
this crazy Irishman that's pushing dope in our section.
He's also been running crap games without our protection.
He has been warned and warned and warned. I think it's
time, Mister Forza, that you go and have a serious talk
with him and show him the error of his ways.'

And I say, 'Don Mario, how serious a talk do you think
it should be?'

And Scordato says, 'A very serious talk. You go ahead
and you do it the way you see fit.'

That to me was a contract. There was no money mentioned. There's never any money mentioned in these
things. You're doing it as a favor, and if there's any
payment later on they give it to you as a favor. So I visit
this gentleman with Butch. His name is Danny Harris. I
go up to him and I says, 'Mister Harris, I'm here repre-
senting Mister Scordato. And he tells me two things:
Number one, he wants a kickback from your crap games
and your card games. Number two, he wants you to stop
running dope around here – and he's very serious about
these matters.'

Harris turns around, being a pretty tough mick in his
own right, and says, 'You tell Mister Scordato to kiss my
ass and don't send no young kids to me. If he wants to talk
to me, let him send some men around, because I'm a man.'

So, I say to the gentleman, 'Okay, Mister Harris, if
that's the way you feel, we won't make any issue about
this, I'll just report to my superiors.'

He says, 'That's a good boy,' and he pats me on the
shoulder. And Butch moves in behind him and sticks a
shank in between his ribs. And he pulls it out and starts
jabbing it in and jabbing it and he kills the guy. Actually,

that's what we were there for, but it showed Butch took the initiative and he wasn't going to be a follower very much longer. He was going to be a man of his own rights.

So, I go back and report to Mister Scordata that he'll have no more problems from Harris. And I tell him how prominent my young friend Butch was in this, because I have to be proud of him for doing this. And Mister Scordato don't show very much emotion, most of them don't. Thank you, he says, and so forth, and we leave.

And we go out and we run around with a few tomatoes and have a few drinks, get into an apartment together and play a couple of wild, crazy games there, like kids do, you know, when they got a few extra bucks. We had a little tomato that was a little older and smarter than we were, sexually, and she liked to show off. I was nineteen then and Butch was sixteen.

A short time later, we get another call from Mister Scordato and Mister Scordato is very unhappy with Louis Taglonetti, one of his own men who's getting a little too big for his britches and is not showing the proper respect. So, the old don tells me to see to it that he don't have any more problems with Taglonetti and make sure that it is done immediately because he is very concerned that may-be this man is building an army against him.

So we go out, Butch and me, and we find out a little information about this guy – where he lives, where his girlfriend lives – everybody's got a girlfriend – and we discover that the only time he's alone is when he's home or at his *goumara's*. 'There's an unwritten rule: you don't hit any man in his own home. I wouldn't want anyone to hit me in my house because if he missed I would turn around and be looking for him in his house. It's just a matter of self-survival.

Well, anyway, we clock him for two or three days to see what his habits are, and we find out that the best time to get Taglonetti is when he goes and stays at his girlfriend's. She lives out in the suburbs of Brooklyn in a one-family house that he's paying for. He leaves there, normally, at three or four o'clock in the morning, and that's when he's alone. So, we lay out there for two nights in a row. One night he don't come out at all. He stays until early morning, which is not good because it's daylight. The next night, it's raining, cold and windy, and Butch and myself are laying down out there, behind the hedges in her front yard. Finally, about twenty-five minutes past four, sure enough the porch light goes on and when the porch light goes on, he opens the door and we wait for him to step out. Butch has got a sawed-off shotgun, double barrel, and I got a thirty-eight snub-nose. As soon as Taglonetti shuts the door behind him, Butch lets go of both barrels and I let go with the thirty-eight and down he goes. I step over to him to make sure that he's dead, because now it's either him or me, and just because you hit him with a shotgun don't mean he died. I put two more in the base of his head and away he goes.

I report this back to Mister Scordata and he's tickled pink. To show his gratitude for doing certain favors for him, the Old Man gives us the area of the city where Taglonetti used to take numbers and horses and sports. So all of a sudden, from being two young punks holding up card games a few years earlier, we became prominent and the word is passed by the Old Man that these two boys got this area. And it's a foregone conclusion that we killed Louis Taglonetti, because no one would be given his section unless it was the same people that knocked him off . .

I get up again because I just can't sit still. I walk in the next room and here's this apple sitting nine-tenths asleep watching one of them television detective programs. And I'm saying to myself, 'My God! Look at these supermen in this program here. They never miss anything, they solve things in sixty minutes that would take Sherlock Holmes six months.' It really would be nice if there were cops like this who could be here right now watching me. Not like these guys. Can you imagine how a well-organized operation like the mob in Brooklyn, if they had an idea where I was, would overthrow a half-dozen of these jerks even with guns in their hands, guys that don't think of anything but drinking and telling dirty stories? They're always complaining, always complaining – not just to me, to Tom Oakes and the supervisor, 'I want to go home or I want some more overtime. Can't you put me down for this and that?'

It's now about quarter after ten. I want to watch the early news to see if there's anything on about me. I walk into my room and I snap the television on and there's the news about me testifying in New York against Don Mario. The reporter says there's a contract for three-quarters of a million dollars on Johnny Forza's head. You know, the FBI gave that to the papers way back before the case got off the ground so that they'd pick it up again right before the trial. It's like brainwashing the jury. They'll think, 'Hey, there's a three-quarter-million-dollar contract on this guy, so what he's got to say is going to be the truth.' And I'm saying to myself, 'Well it *is* going to be the truth, but nobody's going to collect that kind of money. Whoever tries will be dead.' Then they're showing old pictures and sketches of me on the screen. And the marshal next door is saying, 'Hey, you see yourself on television there, John?'

'Oh, yeah, it's terrific. Just what I need. Publicity. Is this the way the Justice Department protects me? Lets these clowns put me on nationwide television? So no matter where I go, I'm going to be made again?'

'Oh, you know John, we can't stop the news media . . .'

'I know you can't do anything except what you want to do,' I say.

The music is drifting up from downstairs in the bar, and they're playing 'Alfie', my favorite song. I wish to Christ they'd stop playing it. Every time I hear some of that soft music it drives me up a tree. Reminds me of things in the past that I don't like to think about. I really don't like to think about them because then I was a super-star in the street. What was it that I didn't have? Whatever I wanted was mine. I got the best tables at restaurants and the best women and the best automobiles and clothes – all hand-made and tailormade. I traveled all over the world first class. All over the country, no matter what big city I went to, I walked over and saw the big boss of that particular city and was greeted with open arms like I was Jesus Christ or something. I'd present myself at hotels and get the finest suite for absolutely nothing. Like visiting royalty. And if I was alone when I got there, someone would be in my room waiting for me – you know, a tomato or something. I lived pretty good. I lived like an important man, a man of respect. Now any made man, a man who's been made a member of the mob can travel on mob business and he'll get special treatment from made men in other towns. Not the red carpet, but they take care of him. It's sort of like belonging to the same church. Funny when you think about it, but we use the same word 'made' when we talk about a cop or someone recognizing us. When you see a guy's eyes open a bit as he looks at you or you catch him staring, well you can be sure he's made you and the only thing that means is trouble.

Right now I'd love to be at the Fontainebleau with my Nancy. Just laying there, not making love to her, just laying there holding her. Planning another trip someplace. Talking about how nice it would be to get away from Carla, divorce her and marry up with my Nancy. But we always knew that was impossible. It's not impossible now, but it was then, when I was on the street. Carla was the daughter of Don Vito Stefano. The Old Man would never have heard of me getting divorced. So I was stuck. I married Carla to jump up on the ladder a little bit and I been sorry since. I would have jumped up on the ladder regardless. I was a somebody on the street. I knocked a couple of guys dead for the mob. I got it made. I didn't really need her. I could have married Nancy and it would be a different story if I went informer like I'm doing now with Nancy as a wife. It would be something to look forward to, being stashed somewhere with Nancy. We could go out and enjoy ourselves. Maybe in South America or Australia or someplace. I wouldn't mind going straight with her as a wife. I can't even consider it now.

When we were together – Nancy and me – I used to pick out her clothes for her, you know? We'd be in Vegas, you sit around near the pool area and they send these models out wearing new bathing suits and new furs and so forth. They say that this is from such-and-such a shop and it costs this much money. And I would actually sit there with my Nancy and have the girls model and I'd say, 'Gee, you like that dress? I think it's terrific. Have that brought to my room in her size.' And I'd give the room number and I'd just sign for it, whatever I liked. And Nancy got the biggest thrill in the world modeling these things for me when we got upstairs to the room. She'd say, 'How does it look? Do you really like it now? Because if you don't like it I won't take it.'

Now she didn't always like what I picked out, but she mostly said she did. She knew I never liked to be crossed. That's the way it was with me and Nancy. I told her everything she did. I'd say, 'Look, I seen a dress in the such-and-such a window, get in there and get that dress. Okay, we're going out tonight, I want you to wear it.'

'I don't like the color,' she might say.

'I don't care if you like the color or not. I like the color, understand? Go and get the dress. Now, if you don't want to get the dress, go take a walk for yourself.' You know mob guys are very cruel to broads in that respect. They push them around because they don't push their wives around. Not that I ever pushed Carla around. I didn't give enough of a damn about her to do that, but giving the girlfriend a hard time is, well, sort of a habit you pick up because you know she can't do nothing about it.

The type of girl that Nancy is, she always knew how to relax me. She knew it a lot easier and better than my wife, not only sexually, but talking and laughing the way she would over a subject so nonchalantly where my wife would make a big issue of it. Sicilian wives are constantly worried. It's their stock in trade, worrying, and they don't get too much enjoyment out of life because of it. But Nancy, she's not worried. She knows she has me on borrowed time and she's willing to make the best of it. If I got a million dollars, let's enjoy it. If I haven't got a quarter, let's enjoy that, too.

Nancy is a real high-style tomato and she knows how to act, and she knows how to keep her mouth shut, which is more important. She was a half-assed singer in a mob-connected joint when I met her. No voice to speak of, but a hell of a body and a good head on her shoulders. She's also very understanding, and that's a big thing. When you need a broad she's got to be understanding. When I'd come home after I'd just been called on the carpet by the Old Man and had my ears chewed up a little bit, I'd be in a bad mood and I might take it out on her. And she was always able to say, 'Well, I understand what's the matter. I mean, go ahead, you want to put me down, go ahead.' And she's sitting around and listening to me complain, 'That son-of-a-bitching boss broke my aggies again today . . .'

But, I tell you I've got so much on my mind I'm not even thinking about her. 'Don't shut me out of your life,' she used to say to me. Well, right now, it don't look like I have much left to shut her out of.

Ah, Butch. When he dropped a dime and set me up for the cops, I should have realized he done it. I should have realized it was Butch while I was still on the street. But you close your eyes when you love somebody, and I don't want to sound like a fairy saying that, but I did love him. I loved the Old Man too. The Old Man took me out of the gutters and put me on top of the pile. And I can't believe that he would let this be done to him – that he would let Butch drop a dime on me, so that the cops would get me and Butch could take my money and my businesses. Once Butch done that – and the Old Man, he had to be in on it – then there was no way out for me. The only thing I could do is what I done. Be an informer. And every time I think about it, I know that Butch is my real problem. He'll look for me forever – and be mad enough to do crazy things.

I remember when Butch and I lived together. It was after we took over Louis Taglonetti's territory. Now that we were settling ourselves into a pretty good thing, Butch and I got an apartment, a three-four-room flat. And we're both single guys and we dress it up, put in a new stereo and color television. One of our agents happened to be a junkie named Jimmy. He was picking up numbers off the street and calling them in to us. See, Butch and I worked in the office. We had two, three phones in there and we sat across the table from each other, taking the numbers and the horses and charting them and so forth. Now, one day we close up shop about three-thirty in the afternoon and we go out, and about seven o'clock I get a call from Butch. He's in a turmoil, full of hate and everything else. And I ask him what's the matter.

'Someone broke into our place,' he says. 'Don't they know they can't do this to us?'

I come over there and it takes about seven minutes to

find out who broke in and stole our stuff. We find out it's the junkie, so I says: 'Okay, now look, this kid is a good runner for us. We know he's got a problem, Butch. Let's go and get him and bring him up here. I'm going to smash him in the face a couple of times. Nothing serious, just something so that he'll remember what he's done,' I said, 'because he's so coked up he don't know what he's doing anyway. Now, I want you to give me your word you'll just let me handle it, because you know we don't want to hurt this guy. He means money to us.'

Butch was furious. He wanted to kill him. So we go out and we find our friend Jimmy and we say, 'Jimmy, we know you took this stuff. We want it back. You bring it back and nothing's going to happen.'

'Okay, I'm sorry. I took it, I sold it to what's-his-name. Here, here's the money . . .'

'Go and get the stuff back, we need the stuff more than we need this lousy two dollars that you sold it for.'

So he does. He goes and gets the stuff, and he's lugging it up the second floor apartment by himself and finally, after he gets it all in, I turn around and say, 'Now, you got to remember that you done this.' And I smash him right across the face. And as I do this I say, 'Now, that's about it. Go to work and mind your business and next time you need a fix, you're in trouble this way, come to us before you go to anyone. Understand?' And I no sooner get the words out of my mouth when Butch whips out a billy club from underneath his jacket and starts beating the kid unmercifully. 'I'm going to kill you, you son-of-a-bitch. You don't show no respect . . .' And he beats him over the head and breaks his collarbone and his nose and fractures his skull. And, if I'm not there, he'd be a dead man, this kid, a dead man. I have to pull Butch off and in the heat of it he even takes a swing at me with the club, and that's a fact.

It was then that I realized he could not be trusted. He

could not trust himself. As smart as he is and everything else, his emotions get the best of him. Later, I found his treachery went farther. He started to branch out on his own, picking up some hijacked stuff and he wasn't kicking in to me. He was kicking in to Old Man Scordato, who takes it but don't like it because he sees that we grew up together but now a little hostility is coming along. Anyway, I hear off the street that there's a load of merchandise floating around and someone's got it. And I find out that Butch's got it and Butch disposed of it and there was no money kicked in. He was getting too big and I had to do something about it. So I met with him one day at the Oasis Lounge on Utica Avenue in Brooklyn, and I bought him a drink and I said, 'Hey, what about that load of cameras you handled last week?'

And he says, 'What about it?'

'What about my piece of it?'

'Hey, Johnny,' Butch gives me the smile, 'didn't I tell you? The Old Man said I didn't have to split with nobody but him on that one, you know?' Now, I knew the Old Man hadn't said any such thing, so I smiled back at Butch and he's yakking away, '. . . so he told me that whatever I come up with at Pan American is . . .' And, I turn as if to order another drink and I suddenly give him the back of my right hand right in the chops. He's dizzy, so I move in and smash him one in the gut. And I walk out of the joint. I didn't beat him with a sap and I didn't knee him. I just had to teach him to obey the rules. That night he came to me as I was eating dinner and apologized, said he knew he done the wrong thing and he was sorry. I don't think he ever forgot the beating. I think he feeds his anger on it now . . .

I'm sitting here and I can hardly breathe. The air in this room is so thick. This broken-down air-conditioning is pre-War Number One. I think Lindbergh had it in his airplane that he crossed the ocean with. It's so warm! I got to get some goddamn air. I don't care if they like it or not. Everything is tight on me. I'm getting soft sitting around these damn rooms, just eating and sweating. Eating and sweating, that's all I do. I got to open this window. I walk to the door again, open it a little and look outside. And the first thing I notice is, it's so quiet. I mean there are no noises out there of any kind. And why is it so dark? That's what I noticed before. There's something missing. I lean out a bit more and try to see if there's anyone around the pool, but I can't see nothing.

That's it. I can't see nothing down there because there's no light. The swimming-pool light. It's out and it's supposed to be on all night. There's definitely something wrong here. You'd think these jerks that I'm with would have noticed it.

'Hey, Mister Oakes!' I yell, and I no sooner say 'Oakes' when an explosion roars across the pool and something is hitting me in the face like buckshot. A shot goes above my head. Two more shots go. I fall to the floor and feel my whole face burning like hot melted lead is being poured into it. Oakes comes running in and throws himself on top of me. Suddenly, I can't see and I can taste blood in my mouth. I try to get up and I get to my knees and, thank God, I can see a little. Mister Oakes helps me up and I can hear running and someone bumps into us and a shot goes off in my right ear. I shake my head and another shot goes off and the window glass smashes. And Oakes is yelling, 'You sons-of-bitches! Be careful! Be careful! Control yourselves!' He's the only one who didn't panic. I lost control myself. I don't give a shit, I am scared. It was a close miss, but they got me. No question about it. God forbid I don't lose my eye. I can't tell if I lost it or I didn't. All I know is my face is a mass of blood and I can't touch it. It feels like a thousand needles jabbing me.

Now, Mister Oakes wraps a towel around my face and pushes me towards the door with his gun drawn. 'Come on, quick! Get out of here before someone throws a bomb now they know where we are.' And we stumble downstairs and get into a car with one other guy. The other marshals stay behind, and Oakes takes off down the highway. 'All right, take it easy, Johnny,' he's telling me. 'It's just splinters. You're going to be okay. Ain't even going to be scarred. You're still going to be pretty.'

Mister Oakes is keeping me under control with his talk. He's cool. He's a pro. And he would have made a hell of a thief. I owe this man my life like I once owed Butch my life. But I know I'll never live to see court. They're going to get me before I go in there. Is there any way I could scream out to them, 'Leave me alone and I'll change my mind! I'll take it all back and tell them I was lying! I'll act crazy and cop an insanity plea! I'll let them put me away for a long bit, if you forgive me and let me back in! I didn't know it was going to be this way!'

Butch might have missed me tonight, but he still got me. This son-of-a-bitch has me thinking that I'm making a very, very big mistake. I wish Nancy was here, I really do. But she's not and you're a big boy now, Johnny Forza, and you better smarten up. You were told to stay away from the window. Why did you go over?

I can picture Butch setting it all up and I smile a little thinking about the cowboy that he picked to do this to me. I can guess it was one of maybe five guys, and they must have told him the motel and then he came in dressed as a delivery man and looked around and went back and told them he could handle it. And when he said 'yes' he got the contract and he put his life on the line. Now that he's failed, he's in serious trouble because they've committed themselves. I know I been shot at, and the police and everybody else knows. So that cowboy's got to feel worse than I do right now.

I'm sitting in this car, and my face is a mass of blood under the towels that Mister Oakes wrapped around my head. My face is burning like I was looking into a fire and it's going to hurt like all hell when they take these towels off me. If I was by myself, I'd be pounding my fist on the wall to take my mind off it. But now, I can feel my anger taking over. I don't care who you are, the toughest guy in the world is scared before the first fright, but then he collects himself. A good street wiseguy can be shitting-in-his-pants scared, but he'll always have enough common sense to do what's necessary to try and survive. I mean, like the first time I got shot, I was driving my car and a car pulled up along side of me and let two shots go. I hit the floor while I was going, you know? I slammed my foot on the brake and then I just went for the floor under the dashboard while the car was going. And they got more scared than I did, and they pulled ahead to get away, the damn fools – because I didn't have a gun with me. And I looked up over this steering wheel and I seen them going, and I was heading off the shoulder. So I just got that damn thing back on the road and, whoosh, I did a U-turn and went the other way, you know? I saw who it was and they were destroyed within a month, both of them.

Mister Oakes picks up his car radio and calls the local office or whatever. He gives them our location and says, 'Where's the closest hospital? I have an emergency here.' And, naturally, he don't say who it is. And they direct him to some town right over the line I never heard of. After a few minutes, he pulls up to this hospital emergency ward and he sends the other guy in there to look around and then he comes running in with me at gunpoint – he keeps his gun showing – and people in the emergency room are scattering. They see this man with a gun in his hand running in with me with blood all over me, and they don't know from nothing. So he shows his badge and they let me lay down there and he says, 'Just take care of him, we'll explain what happened later.' Doctors come hurrying over and start working on me. Give me a shot right off the bat for pain. And they clean me up and get as many splinters as they can out.

They get me out of there in less than an hour, and now we're supposed to go back and find another motel because we're not due in court until tomorrow. Mister Oakes is about as smart as a street guy. 'The hell with this, John,' he says, 'Why should we go back to that motel or any other motel? It's just a question of time before they find you. We have to be in court at ten o'clock in the morning. Let's go in tonight.'

He stops the car at a gas station and gets out to make a call. The guy in the back speaks up, 'How do you feel, Johnny? You all right?'

'Yeah, I'm fine,' I tell him.

'Don't worry, we're going to take care of you ...'

'You're going to take care of me?' I say. 'You're the son-of-a-bitch that almost shot me in the back!'

'No, it wasn't me,' he says. 'It was Wayne. You know, the black marshal there. He got a little bit nervous and he thought he seen someone out there on the patio shooting at you and he shot at him.'

I says, 'He almost hit me, the son-of-a-bitch' I says, 'Maybe he's getting paid for it.'

'No, no, he's not. Don't say that. We don't go for that shit.'

'I don't care if you go for it or not,' I say. 'I almost got shot in the back,' I say. 'Look at my face. I almost got shot in the front. How many angles do I have to take it from?'

Mister Oakes comes back to the car shaking his head. He's called the U.S. Attorney in charge of this case and told him to speak to the security police in charge of the Federal Court House and let them know we're going to come in there. But the plan gets turned down. 'Sorry,' they say, 'we can't let him into the courthouse. He's on

35

his own.' So Mister Oakes decides that we have to stay someplace for a little while, and he drives me to the house of a friend of his in New Jersey, another United States Marshal. And we stay in the basement of this house, just sit around and I'm laying on a couch thinking that tomorrow we got to go into Foley Square, downtown Manhattan, and that's a bad place for me.

So I say, 'You think there's any way to postpone this thing? You know, because I got hurt?'

'John, there's no way in the world,' he says. 'If you don't go into this court, you're definitely going to be thrown to the wolves. They'll throw you right back in a cell in an open prison and say, "Here he is, boys, he's a nice tender piece of meat. Eat him up." ' I got to agree. They would send me back, they as much as said so, and I wouldn't last ten minutes back in jail. I hate to admit it, but I got to go through with this. If I don't, I'm going to be a dead man anyway.

He says, 'Well, I think maybe tomorrow morning we better take you in – oh, maybe in a mail truck or something. I'll figure something out by morning.'

And I'm thinking, 'Mister Oakes makes it all sound so easy and like there's nothing to it. Maybe he's just trying to keep me cool.' But whatever he figures out better be good, because those animals out there are figuring right now how to stop me from getting up on that witness stand and sending them all up for hijacking. They've been figuring for months.

# CHAPTER TWO

About six-thirty in the morning, Mister Oakes wakes me up. He gives me a couple of tranquilizers to calm me down, and we sit around and have a little coffee there in the basement. 'John, I'm not going to tell you not to be nervous,' he says. 'That's ridiculous. I'm scared myself, and I'm just guarding you. But we're going in with the best of it. We're going to take you in a mail truck and there'll be ten marshals watching you. I'm going to send in two different decoys – people who look like you. I got one Treasury guy and another guy in the FBI and they'll ride in at half-hour intervals so that whoever's looking for you won't be sure which is you.'

While he's going over this, I'm saying to myself, 'Butch ain't going to go for this. He's not that stupid, to go for the first person that comes in.' Besides, whoever he's going to have behind a rifle or hand grenade is going to be someone that knows me well enough so that he ain't going to be fooled by no guy with a hat and a pair of sunglasses.

Because these guys are old hats at this. They done it before, outside a court, inside, it don't matter. Like the time they sent that New York Irish guy up to Boston to whack out a pigeon in the armoured-car robbery. The guy shoots the pigeon with a machine gun outside the court and, cool as you please, takes the gun apart, puts it in his little leather briefcase, and walks right down the street past the cops. Or the time they bring the witness in Miami into the Federal courthouse in a plain car through the delivery truck door. He's safe inside and someone rolls a grenade under the car – blows it apart and him with it.

Now, I can think about this kind of stuff until the cows

37

come home and get myself to where I won't want to set foot outside this room. So I got to forget it and just figure that Mister Oakes knows what he's doing and make like this is just another day and I got to get ready to go out.

'... because there's no question,' Oakes is saying, 'they're going to be looking for you. I mean, they know you're coming and there's nothing we can do about it. And they also know they got to whack you now or at least make an attempt. So, we're going to send in one decoy at eight-thirty and one about quarter past nine. You're due on the stand at ten, and you're going in at five minutes to. By that time,' he says, 'everybody will think that you've been in there for a while.'

I take a shower and clean up and take off the bandages, and Mister Oakes gives me a little makeup to put on so that these things on my face wouldn't show up so much. You can bet the DA's going to want to see me cleaned up. They don't want me looking like I got beat up, looking as though the information that I'm about to give was brutally taken away from me or anything like that.

And now the marshals are as nervous as I am, I can see that. 'How are we going to do this, Mister Oakes?' They're asking the same questions that I'm asking because they don't know any more than me. Like always, Mister Oakes is in control of the whole thing. He is the only one that knows what he's going to do. And I can suggest, but I can't have anything to say. He makes some phone calls and arranges for more marshals to meet him at a pickup spot. And then he explains to one of his men, 'You're going to take in the first guy, Sam, from the IRS. He'll be dressed in a dark blue suit. Keep his hat and sunglasses on so it'll look as though he's Johnny Forza trying to disguise himself. And when you get near the gate, go like hell, make your tires screech. Attract some attention. Maybe we'll have a squad car in front of you with its sirens on.'

I'm listening to this and all I know is if I was sitting on the other side there laying for Johnny Forza, I'd know he's got to go through this gate or he's got to go through the front door. And I would definitely have someone with a scope rifle a couple of buildings away. I mean they ain't going to pay no attention, they can't search everyplace, they're not even trying. I'm not the President of the United States that they're going to check all buildings around. If I get lucky and live through it, fine. If I don't – see you later, sucker.

So, maybe it's a good idea that Oakes has decided to send another guy in. Because if I was in Butch's shoes I would make it my business that the people that are going to do the damage get some connections with the court security, so they'll get a tip when we're coming. All of a sudden I'm getting these thoughts in the back of my mind – I don't know whether you call them flashbacks or what – of last night, and how Butch almost got me, and of that other time in the can, the first time he tried. I was in there walking towards the shower room and I thought I was alone and I heard a little noise and looked around and there were a couple of black guys with shanks that started to come after me. I hit one and he slipped and fell on the floor, and I'm running down the corridor naked, trying to get away from the other one, and a screw comes in and stops it. From then on I knew the finger was on me. The guys went in the hole and got transferred to another joint. It's not robbery when all you got on you is a towel.

The more I think of it, if there was any way out of this, I would definitely take it. But knowing them the way I do, there's definitely no way out – no way at all. I'm still thinking to myself, 'What if I run out of here? Give these guys the shake, disappear, and the government can't come to trial without a witness.' You know, there's an old tradition we call intercession. It means when you get in real trouble with the mob you can take it on the lam and ask a friend to go to bat for you with the Old Man, sort of plead your case and tell why you done what you done and why he should maybe forgive and forget. And if the guy is good, maybe the Old Man lets you live. Now, I find myself thinking of guys I could ask to speak for me – but it's impossible. I didn't just do the wrong thing, I did a mortal sin. But wait. Suppose I get on the stand and say I can't remember their names or I'm not sure if I ever seen that guy before. Would the mob let me alone then? Would they let me leave the country? I know the answer. There's no way they would let me live. They'd promise me anything if I changed my mind but I'd end up being put to sleep. I already gone too far. I can't go back.

So, mister, you better spruce yourself up, you better go in there and you better tell them the truth and you better convince this jury. Because if this DA don't think you're trying, he'll throw you right back to the wolves, just like Mister Oakes says. And I start thinking about that. They don't have no more capital punishment in New York State, but for me to go to jail again is an automatic death sentence. I mean, if the judge says, 'I'm holding you in contempt and I'm sending you back to jail,' or the government says, 'We are pulling the rug out from under you, Mister Forza, you didn't do exactly what we wanted you to do, and the hell with you anyway because you're a criminal. We're sending you back to jail.' I mean, that's just like saying what time I'm going to get killed, because it wouldn't be two days until someone discovered who I was and passed the word out. How long would I last? Half an hour? Two hours? No more than twenty-four hours, that's for sure. And the killing in there would be worse than getting hit with a slug out here. God knows what they would do. Strangle me. Burn me. Throw gasoline from the workshop on me and drop a match. In the can, you don't walk near the edges of the walls where someone could drop something on you from the second tier. You walk in the middle of the aisles and you're looking up over your head, and what is it for them to drop something on you – a locker or something hits you on top of the head and it kills you, splits your head like a melon.

Butch wouldn't even have to order it. They would hit me because it's a matter of principle to hit me. I mean, everyone who's there is going to say, 'Listen, I'm doing fifteen years. Who's this guy to walk away because he opened his mouth? That's not the right way to play the game.' So they don't care what the reasons are behind it. You take a guy that's doing life, maybe double life, what does he care if he gets one more life? You see? And that's number one. Number two, someone that's due to hit the street soon would imagine in that back of his mind that he's doing a big favor for the Old Man. And when he gets out he says, 'While I was in there they sent Johnny Forza back in and I'm the guy that planted him.' And he might be well received for it. Depends of course on who he is and who he knows.

I say to Mister Oakes, 'Don't they have an area where the judges park their cars? A side entrance where no one else is allowed?' He says, 'Yes.'

And I say, 'Why can't we go in there? They'd never be watching that.'

'There isn't a judge that's going to let you do it,' he says. 'Get it through your head, you're not going to get help from anybody except what you got right here. I'm going to help you all I can, because I like you a little bit and because I think it's my duty.'

You know, I'm sitting there listening to him, and I'm thinking, 'I got to face these people in court and I don't really know if I am going to be able to answer when they ask me these questions because I don't think I can bring myself to do these things. I don't know where I'm going to

41

get the balls to do it.' It's not that I'm yellow, it's just that there's no one going to be in there who's on my side. Who am I going to look at, in that courtroom, to get a friendly look? Who? That's what I want to know. Who am I going to look at? . . .

About an hour later we're down to Foly Square. A van is pulling up to the rear gates of the courthouse. It's like a paddy wagon, and out of the back, like in an army picture, the doors swing open and ten state cops jump out, dressed exactly alike with the boots and the boy scout hats and with shotguns and machine guns. They line up facing each other where the cars are going to come into the gate, on both sides of the driveway, one about every five feet. I'm about number three in line on the right-hand side, facing away from the back of the building. I'm dressed exactly the same as them. I got shades on like the rest of them. But I'm sweating through the uniform because I know someone is up on one of these buildings watching this whole thing through a high-powered rifle scope. Just waiting. I know of a dozen people that are able to part your hair from two, three hundred yards away with a thirty-oh-six with scope on it. I mean this is their job. That's why they're on the payroll for five hundred dollars a week from the mob. They got balls, they got eyesight, and they got the best equipment there is going.

So I'm standing there wondering to myself if that guy that's looking down that rifle barrel can see the sweat on my shirt. I must stick out different from these cops. No question, I don't look the same. Can you imagine me in a cop's uniform? How low down I got! I never thought I'd get this low in my whole life. My God! I hope nobody sees me dressed like this. Maybe that's why Mister Oakes did this. No one who ever knew me would think that I would dress like a cop. Also, I'm thinking, Wouldn't

42

it be terrific if this machine gun was loaded! I could let all these turkeys have it and get out of here.

And now I'm worrying, because they can give me a completely new face and new hairline, and a uniform, but they can't change my build or my motions, the way I walk. Frankie Barba had arms that used to hang down almost to his knees, you know. I mean, what are they going to do, cut six inches off his arms? In the back of my mind is always, 'Listen, that guy up there with a telescopic rifle is taking a good look at me, he knows my walk.' So I try to change my walk a little bit. But that won't make no difference, he knows what my back looks like, what the back of my neck looks like. They say you can change a man's face but you can always tell him by the back of his neck. Just changing the hat and the suit doesn't make a hill of beans. You know, it's hard to fool a top head-hunter, they got eyes like a hawk and they notice little things no one else would – your ears, how far apart your eyes are. They got to, it's their life. A lot of these guys are a little weird – they sit around staring at the wall and concentrating, mapping out the score in their head. Most of them you'd never suspect. I know one looks like a hippie kid – long hair, droopy mustache, blue jeans, sandals, the works. And there was Buster from Chicago, used to work a lot for Vito Genovese. Hell of a hit man and he looked like Joe College. The thing you notice about all of these guys is that they don't talk much and they're cool, very, very cool. They're careful and they plan things and they don't make a move unless they know just what they're gonna do.

Now, you see, things are really happening fast. It only seems slow to me because I'm really worried about being hit. Mister Oakes set this thing up perfectly. As soon as we get lined up and get ourselves paced off we're looking at all the surrounding buildings with automatic

43

weapons and shotguns ready – wham – the gate is opened and three cars come flying down the alley and in the courtyard. In the front car are two United States Marshals in plain clothes. In between is another car with three people in it. And in back another car with two more. The marshals in the front and back cars jump out with guns in their hands and they're looking all around and the state cops start being alert with their guns, looking around at all the buildings. I keep looking straight ahead. I don't want to face up. I really don't want to see anything. Then someone says, 'Okay, come on.' And Mistress Oakes jumps out of the middle car and he grabs ahold of the decoy – the other guy dressed like I would be dressed with a hat and sunglasses and a little beard – and he pulls him out of the front seat and they start running for the doorway.

He's running and I hope he makes it. On the other hand, I really don't. Maybe if they whack him it'd take the pressure off of me. It's a hell of a thing to say. The poor sucker's trying to help me. But he's got to be a sucker, I mean for what he's getting for a week's pay to stand out there and look to catch one in the back of the head, he's cuckoo. This getup I'm wearing probably fools nobody, but the idea is that it throws them off long enough to give me a chance to get in and get out. Let me put it to you this way, if there was any doubt in that guy's mind up in the building there, he'd shoot anyway, because what the hell does he care? One stiff is as well as another to him, and he might hit the right guy.

Now, they're in the door and we're forming a double line and following them inside. I don't fit in with these cops, that's for sure. When I went into the van coming over no one said anything to me. They all stared at me. You really couldn't see too much with the mirror shades on. That's the worst thing in the world, when you can't see someone's eyes you can't figure what they're thinking. But no one offered me a cigarette. They knew who I was. Maybe they didn't like the idea of my being there. Maybe they didn't like the idea of risking their lives for me. And maybe they say, 'Who the hell's this son-of-a-bitch? Who is this guy to get such special privileges to wear our uniform?' And I feel like saying, 'Hey, this wasn't my idea. I don't like it any more than you do.'

Anyway, we get lucky enough to get in the door, and as soon as we get inside, Mister Oakes comes over and says, 'Johnny, you done terrific. Have a cigarette.' He's a pretty cute operator. He's cooling me off so that I won't be a nervous wreck for the trial. And he's congratulating everybody for getting in there. I got to admit it was a good show of strength. They're not trying to impress the mob, but there may be a crazy cowboy around there with a Saturday-night special trying to make a name for himself. If he sees ten or twelve guards there and so forth, he might back away from it.

Now that we're in, the first question I have in my mouth is, 'How are we going to get out?' Mister Oakes says, 'We're inside and we got all day to figure out how we're going to get out of here. I got a few ideas.' He's not a bullshit artist. He did say we got all day to figure. That means he's not saying it's going to be a cakewalk. He's saying, 'Don't worry about it. We'll do our best.' And his best is pretty good.

'Be careful when we get in the elevator, Mister Oakes,' I say, 'Someone upstairs could force open the doors and drop a hand grenade right down on top of us. It'd be nothing to signal and say, "Hey, they got in the elevator." Down you go, caught between floors, you ain't got a chance.' And Mister Oakes tells me, 'You're right, the only trouble is that they can't start or operate these doors without a key and we got the only key.'

And I say, 'Listen, they have locksmiths by the dozen to make keys, master keys. They have a machine called a key gun, and they stick it into the lock, and just keep

45

pressing the trigger, and in a matter of minutes the lock opens. We used to have one.'

And he tells me, 'Don't worry about it. I got men stationed on each floor. Nobody can get near this elevator.' So, I'm saying to myself, 'What a relief. This guy is half-ways on the ball.' So we go to the elevator and a marshal sticks a key in there and the door opens up. This is a private elevator for bringing up witnesses, dangerous criminals, and so forth, and nobody has access to it but the marshals.

In the meantime, the state police come, and the head of them – the sergeant – says, 'Okay, boys, get up through the corridors. Let everybody see you. I want them to know we are ready for war here. You know, that we can produce as many men as they can, better armed than they can. If you see anyone looks suspicious say, "What you got there, mister? Identify yourself." Know what I mean?'

Mister Oakes turns the elevator key, the doors close, and the thing starts to move and I'm thinking every second that it's going to stop . . . it's going to stop . . . now, it's . . . and it jerks a little and it feels like it's slowing down and I lean back in the corner away from the door and wait for it to stop. I'm sure that someone on top there is going to open the trapdoor on the roof of this thing and spray us with bullets. The elevator finally stops. I look up, holding my breath – and, the doors open. There's two marshals outside, one looks to the right, one looks to the left. They got automatic weapons with them right inside the courthouse. And they say, 'Okay, come on.' And Mister Oakes says, 'Take a right.' We take a right, walk down two, three doors and open a door with a key. Mister Oakes says, 'Stand right here.' He goes inside with his gun in his hand and looks around, comes back out. 'Okay, bring him in.' In we go, the other guys with me, and they shut the door. There's another two men inside. Mister Oakes tells them, 'Okay, boys, you two guys stand out front. No one comes in or out unless you personally know them or you tell me about it. If someone comes up and says, "I'm the U.S. Attorney," I want to see him, say, "Mister, you just wait right here." Be careful. These guys are no suckers. Meanwhile,' he tells one of the other marshals, 'you go down to the car and get his suitcase and bring it up so he can get out of this uniform.'

And about seven or eight minutes later, there's a knock on the door, Mister Oakes goes and opens it up a little and a marshal says, 'The U.S. Attorney's here. He wants to speak to him.' Well, Mister Oakes knows who he is and lets him in. And by that time they bring some coffee and the guy's telling me what to expect.

'You walk in there and those lawyers are going to hammer away at you. Just tell the truth. Look at the jury when you give the important answer. Let them look in your eyes to see that you're telling the truth.' Well, this guy's a young fella. Looking to make a few notches by putting away one of these Mustache Petes. He's not dressed too sharp. Fact his clothes are a little rumpled because DA's don't make good money and, like I said, a young fella, glasses, kind of shy looking, with a lot of ambition. And he's sitting down and he's talking to me and he's calling me 'Mister Forza' because maybe he's trying to get on the good side of me. And he's telling me, 'You know, these people are going to hammer away.'

And I'm saying to myself, 'You punk, I know more about going into court than you do.' And I listen to all this bullshit and I tell him, 'Look, I know what I got to do. Don't try and read me like a script to an actor. I'm going in there. You're going to ask me a question, I'm going to tell you the truth as I see fit. Please don't try and tell me what to do. Because I'm only going to get mixed up. I'll look at the jury when I think I can look at the jury. I might not be able to look at them. I might feel guilty.' I'm telling this to the guy because I do feel guilty. I'm doing

47

something now that I been taught all my life not to do. All of a sudden, I'm doing it. Is that right?

So he says, 'Okay, calm down...'

And I say, 'Now, I want to ask you a few questions. How long do you think we're going to be in there? Because I got to figure out how the hell we're going to get out of there.' Mister Oakes is saying the same thing. We'd like some sort of an idea when I'm going to get off the stand. So the prosecutor says, 'Well, it shouldn't take me much more than an hour and a half to question him and then about another hour to cross-examine and maybe a rebuttal of another fifteen or twenty minutes and so forth. And, maybe figure you can get him out of there about an hour after the noon recess. Okay?'

Meantime, I'm getting dressed to go in there. Trial's going to start in about ten minutes. It's been going on for two days now. I'm the star witness, but the prosecutor's been building this case very careful. He's trying to prove a conspiracy for organized hijacking and I'm supposed to clinch it for him. Well, the DA shakes my hand and says, 'I know you'll do right for us. Good luck.' And pats me on the back like I was some animal being led out to the slaughter, you know? And away he goes, saying to himself, 'I'm going to win this case. Am I going to get someplace!' He's not worried about me. He's not being nice to me because he likes me, he's being nice to me because he got to use me just like everybody else that used me in the government.

Mister Oakes gets all the marshals in the room where I am. He wants to show me that he's got a lot of power here. So he says, 'Okay, Benson, you and O'Neill go and stay on the left-hand side of the courtroom in the spectators' area. Sit down amongst them. And you two fellas stay over there. I want two more outside the courtroom door. And, ah, me and two others will usher Mister Forza in.' Oakes is giving out orders like an Army commander.

'Now, I think you better go ahead and get yourself settled down there. And have one guy at the metal detector.' You have to have permission to put up a metal detector in a courtroom. Sometimes the judge don't want to do it because it prejudices the jury. They see that metal detector and say, 'Hey, this guy's in danger of his life, here, this witness.' And a lot of judges, what they'll do is keep it outside roped off. But the marshals don't particularly like that because someone could go through it and then be slipped a gun after that. So, anyway, he tells his marshals that we have permission from the judge to have a metal detector up. 'Ah, make sure that everybody goes through it. Any hint of all of a buzzer, you put that guy up against the wall and shake him down right to his toes. Don't let him give you any bullshit "It's my watch." You shake him down, because it could be anything.'

Well, now it comes time to go – and I don't really want to. I wish the judge would drop dead or the jury all get sick or something. I'm sweating it out here and I'm thinking of what's going to become of me and I don't like it. I don't like it at all because I know the best I can hope for is catching a couple in the back of the head first. So Mister Oakes says, 'Well, are you ready to go in now? They're going to be calling you any minute now. Let's walk down to the door.'

I say, 'Okay.' And I'm feeling like the door leads to the gas chamber or the electric chair. Why is Oakes in a hurry? Remember now, I'm testifying against my one-time boss, friend, second father, and hero, you know? The Old Man. And I'm saying to myself, 'I can't do it. I know when I get up on that stand and I look at him, not even out of fear, out of respect, I'm going to freeze.'

And all of a sudden I'm remembering the night I was made. There's no such thing as flashpaper or any of that foolishness. When you're made you go before a board of all Mustache Petes – old-timers like Profaci and

49

Columbo. First, someone's got to sponsor you. Scordato was my sponsor, and after a while he brings me into a room and says, 'This is my friend, this is my blood, this is my son, this is my brother, we eat off the same table...' These are some words that they mumble over you, mumbo jumbo, and all it means is, 'I trust this guy and I want him in the mob.' And believe me, you're sweating it out because you're waiting for them to vote on you, but it's all been cut and dried. If they wasn't going to vote you in, you never would have got inside to see who the rest of them were in the first place. You see what I mean? You say, 'Well, Jesus Christ! What if they let me in there and then they don't like me, what's going to happen?' Well, if they let you in there and didn't like you, believe me, you wouldn't get out, you'd be dead. You would get the kiss of death, *o vache de morta,* you would get. But I have never heard of anyone getting inside the room and being turned down, never once. So anyway, Scordato brings me in and says, 'I sponsor this man, he's my godson now,' and they ask me questions : 'Would you die for us? Do you love us?' and so forth. And naturally I say yes to everything. 'Your life depends on your silence, you will never be able to talk about what took place here or who's in here on threat of your own life and that of your sponsor, Mister Scordato.' And you know that you're in with some very, very serious people. They don't smile. And then they perform the only ritual that there really is to it, they take a little knife and prick your finger and draw a little blood and some from Mister Scordato's finger and just mix it and rub it together. That's the end of the whole ceremony, and they just give you a lot of orders of what's right and what ain't right, and it boils down to one thing : Mister, you got a license to go out and steal now, and we're going to stand behind you. But don't forget to kick your end in. And if you get caught, you're on your own. That's all it means.

I'm remembering this, and all of a sudden I says to myself, 'This son-of-a-bitch. It's him and Butch that done this to me.' It was more likely Butch and not him, and I know that somehow Butch has turned the Old Man against me, poisoned Don Mario's mind and made him think that I'm up here doing the wrong thing for no reason. But, if he has his chance, this Old Man, he'd cut my gizzard out, right on top of the stand, chew it and spit it out. This is what they'd do to me. So now I got myself psyched up and I want to go in there. I want to go in. I want to fight with this guy personally. I want to show him he shouldn't have done me dirty like everybody else has. He should have asked me why I did what I did.

Now, it's time and they walk me out. Before I get to my seat, the witness box, I have to go directly by the lawyers' tables. The lawyers for the prosecution and the lawyers for the defense are sitting there, plus the guy that I'm going to testify against. So I fast glance over there and sure enough the Old Man has caught my eye right off the bat. And he's trying to shake me down mentally. His eyes are not blinking. He's just staring at me. I pay no attention to him. I do pay attention, but I don't want anybody to know it. I can feel myself walk straighter and I try and tighten my face cause I don't want the Old Man to see me like this. I can feel him looking at me and I hope my face don't turn red or nothing and I can almost hear him talking to me, telling me what I done wrong and what I done right and teaching me always what it means to be a man of respect. I remember the Old Man telling me years ago, 'Don't show your emotions – ever. Keep a blank face all the time. Don't let anyone know you're mad or happy. Never show anger, no matter what. That way they cannot have an advantage on you . . .' And I'm trying to look at him with no emotion, but I can't keep my eyes still like he does. I got to blink because they feel like they got dust in them.

Straight ahead of me is the jury – fourteen people in their box looking at me down the end of their noses. I try not to face them when I'm walking.

Finally I get there and I sit down and they put a microphone in front of me. They don't want to miss nothing, naturally. In the first couple of minutes that I'm there, I'm squirming in my seat, trying to get comfortable. And it's hard. It's hard because I know that everyone in the courtroom, including the people from the Justice Department, hate my guts. As nice as they're trying to be to me, they really do hate me because they figure, here's a guy that we have to take care of and he should be on the other side of the fence with the other guys. 'Why give him a break? Because he's talking about *them*? Let them kill him. We couldn't care less.' And I look out there into the audience, or the spectators as I should call them, and I see reporters, writing things down, whatever's being said. And there's a girl that's out there doing sketches of me and everybody else in there and she's looking up over her glasses and smiling at me – like I really feel in the mood to smile.

And now I get a good look at the defense, my boss. The Old Man is sitting there looking the same as always – steel-gray hair combed back neat, steel-rim glasses, not an ounce of fat on him. Don Mario Scordato. Seventy-two and looks sixty. He's the most impressive man in the room, including the judge. He's in his old black suit with a white shirt and a black tie and I know that the only jewelry he's got on is an old gold wristwatch and a plain wedding ring. And under his shirt he's got a little gold cross. And he's looking at me as much as to say, 'How can you do this to me? What did I do to you? You're not supposed to do this. This isn't the way the game is played.' And he's right. I shouldn't be doing this to him of all people, and I can't look at him anymore.

And all his men are my ex-friends sitting in the back

out there. They're not doing anything, but they're dying to catch my eye. But, naturally, I'm trying not to look in their eyes. I look down and I look sideways. I look everywhere. I look up at the clock. I look at the ceiling. I look at the judge. I look everywhere except into their eyes – because if I look into their eyes I'm going to be scared.

Now comes the man with the book, 'Name?'

'John Forza.'

'You will solemnly swear to tell the truth and all, and so forth and so on?'

I put my hand on the book and I say, 'I do.' And they start talking to me and they ask me a question. They ask me my name and where I live. And I say, 'I refuse to answer to protect myself.'

'Why do you refuse to answer?'

'Because I want to stay alive.' And a defense lawyer is on his feet screaming, 'Objection!' The judge looks down, 'Sustained.' And the guy who was asking me says, 'Be seated.' Now, the lawyer for the government there gets up. 'Your name, in fact, is John Forza? Formerly the John Forza of 1456 Ocean Parkway in Brooklyn?'

'Yes.'

'And at one time were you arrested for armed robbery?' The guy wants to bring out all the bad stuff. He wants the jury to hear it from me and from him, these things I done wrong, because then maybe they won't think I'm trying to hide anything. Damn sure he knows as soon as the defense gets hold of me they're going to spring everything. He says, 'You were accused of extortion and convicted and got five years?'

'Yes.' Now, all of a sudden, I notice my mouth is so dry from being scared and nervous that if I was spitting, I'd spit chalk. It ain't that I've done any talking yet. I feel like reaching over to the judge's desk and taking a glass of his water right off there. The judge don't ever crack a smile. He don't ever show the slightest expression in his eyes or anything.

'Now, you're a witness for the government against Mister Scordato here?'

'Yes, I am.'

'Why are you a witness for the government?'

'Well, they done me wrong and so forth.' The defense is yelling out : 'Objection! Objection!'

'What are you objecting too?' the judge asks.

'This is presumption that they wronged him. He doesn't know that they wronged him. Nobody else knows any such thing. It's his say-so. Shouldn't be admitted.' The judge says, 'Sustained.' And he's going to tell the jury to disregard that last remark, take it out of their heads completely. And he's going to say, 'Mister Forza, please don't answer a question thoroughly while someone's objecting. Wait until the objection's over.'

So far, I'm telling the truth and I'm going to tell the truth except maybe for leaving some people out of this who never done me any harm, you know. And, I'm wondering who they already had up here and what the hell they said and if they put in any other stuff from wiretaps or hidden cameras. You come into a case that's been on for a couple days and it's like seeing the middle of a movie — you wonder how it started and how it's going to end.

And they start questioning me again. Places I used to live. Names. The same question maybe seven different times to see if I'm lying, to see if I make a mistake or anything. And all the time, I'm saying to myself : 'Is it worth it? Is it worth it that I'm going to be on the run for the rest of my life?' I know the government isn't going to stand by me forever. They did relocate me and the wife out in Arizona under the name Carpi with phony papers to prove it and a guard on the house. But they told me that after a year or so, or if I don't do what they say, they'll pull out and let me make it on my own if I can. And even if they did stick by me, they ain't half as smart as these guys that are trying to stare me down. You see?

'Is there anyone in this courtroom you know?'

'Objection!'

'What do you object to?' the judge says.

'When he says, "Is there anyone in this courtroom he knows," there could be a dozen people in this courtroom he knows.' Which is right. What the prosecutor should have said is, 'Is there anyone in particular that you know in this place? That you dealt with before you got into trouble?' Or, 'Can you pick out such and such a name in this room?' Things like that.

Judge rules, 'Sustained,' because of that and tells the prosecutor he has to rephrase the question. And the prosecutor gets up from his table, walks around a little bit, says, 'Okay, Mister Forza, is there anybody in this courtroom that you were employed by before?'

'Objection!'

Judge says, 'What are you objecting for? He hasn't said anything outside of that and he has to answer yes or no.'

'Well, it's detrimental to my client. If he does point out my client and says that he worked for him, it's just his word against my client's.'

The judge says to me, 'You can answer that.'

And I turn around and say, 'Yeah, that fella right over there, Mister Scordato, is the fella I used to work for.' But in my mind I'm thinking, when you're with the *le patrone* you're not employed. You don't work for him like he was a company or something, it's a very special relationship. When someone asks you who you're with, he's really asking which boss are you under, who are you pledged to obey? You earn money *for* the boss, you see, you actually support him. He allows you to come under his protection, he allows you to use his name, and for that you have to compensate him with the money that you earn by doing

55

these things. You don't have no social-security number. You might have normal employment records in some front job, you know? You pay homage to him, it's as simple as that. I mean for allowing you to serve him, you pay homage to him and forevermore you protect his rights and his property and his name. This is more important than anything – his name – more important to him than his property, than his money, than anything else. And for that right he allows you to earn a living, a good one, as long as you take care of him.

And the defense is objecting again. 'How do you know? How can you prove that you worked for him? How do we even know that my client knows you?'

And the prosecutor is saying, 'Your honor, are we going to go through this all day? Is this man going to object to every question? Doesn't the court have better things to do than that?' And, they object again, his line of questioning, his insinuations – and they scream and ask for mistrials and so forth. Anyway, by the time I get down to any meat of it, what I'm here to testify about whether I was given a load of stolen whiskey and I say, 'Yes.'

'Who'd you get it from?'

'I got it from Butch.'

'Objection! Who's to say he did get it from Butch? It's just his say-so.'

Well, they keep pounding at me. The prosecutor asks a question. Three objections. 'Can we approach the bench, your honor?' It moves very slow and I lose track of it. Finally, after about an hour of questioning like this I get a little break. The judge, all of a sudden, decides he's got to go to the bathroom and he gets up. As soon as the judge gets up everybody stands up, naturally. So he calls a recess, and as soon as he goes out, Mister Oakes whips me around and through the little door and out to the corridor and back to that room. He says, 'Want anything, John?'

56

'Yeah, I don't want no coffee. How about a cold drink?' Because now my throat and mouth are so parched that I don't know whether I'm coming or going.

'How do you feel?' says Mister Oakes.

'I'm very nervous about it. I mean, it's just started and I'm very nervous.'

And, he says, 'You got the worst of it over with now. You been able to face these people, you been able to look at them . . .' And I say to myself, 'Bullshit, I been able to look at them. Every time I look up and I see the Old Man was looking at me, I want to crawl underneath the chair, or pick it up and throw it out into the audience there and yell, "You son-of-a-bitches, you ruined me and now you're mad at me?"'

Meantime, the prosecutor runs up, knocks on the door, and a marshal lets him in. 'You're doing terrific, John, you really are,' he says. 'Now, in a few minutes, I'm going to give you up to the defense.'

I say, 'I don't like that when you say you're going to "give me up" to the defense.'

'No, John. You know what I mean.'

'Yeah, I know what you mean, you're going to give me up to the defense, don't worry about it. You ain't bull-shitting me.'

He says, 'Well, be careful of this lawyer, because he's a little smarter than the other lawyers. And there's one thing that you said that I'm sure they're going to harp on. When you said that this man was your boss. He'll jump all over you about that. He'll say, "How can you prove he was your boss? You have any payroll records? Can you produce anybody who says he was your boss?"'

'And I'm just going to say he was my boss.'

The guy doesn't answer me. He's all excited about laying it out. He says, 'The defense attorney is never going to say, "Boss of what?" Because then you could turn around say he was a mob boss. I can't ask, "Was he a mob boss?"‚because they'll object ten times over. So, the defense will try to say, "What company did you work for?" And you're going to say, "Well, I had no payroll checks, but ... "And he's going to yell, "Answer the question! Just answer the question!" And he'll turn and say, "Ladies and gentlemen of the jury, you see what kind of man this is, he can't give a straight answer at any time. He's an out-and-out liar. Isn't it true that you lied before?" '

This donkey is beginning to sound just like the defense lawyer and I'm sweating and he's pounding away. I ask Mister Oakes if I can have a couple more of the pills that the doctor prescribed for me at the Public Health Clinic. What they are is tranquilizers, but I hate for the guy to know that I'm so upset. So Mister Oakes says, 'Certainly, John. Here. Here's some water.' He's glad to give them to me because he wants me to calm down. And the prosecutor is saying to me, 'Now, John, when you go in there, they're going to pound away at your credibility and all you have to do is tell the truth.' And he's telling me, 'That other lawyer there won't yell. He's very soft-spoken, but he'll try and trick you. He'll try and be a friend of yours in the court. He'll get up to you and he'll say, "Hey, John, how are you? Don't be nervous. I don't mean you any harm." And all the time he's more deadly than the other guy.'

So, after about fifteen minutes, I'm lugged back into the court and the judge isn't back yet, but Mister Oakes tells me to take my seat and I walk in and sit in the stand there. It seems like hours before the judge comes out and I'm sitting here just thinking of what the Old Man feels like. What does he feel like, imagining that I'm doing this for no reason? At least, if he knew, if I could only get to him in a room and say, 'Listen, I'm doing this here because I was forced into doing it. This was the reason I was forced into doing it, you know.' I know it wouldn't do

58

me any good, but I'd like to be able to look in his eyes and see some understanding. He has no idea in his mind that Butch done this to me. In my opinion, if the Old Man knew that Butch done this he would eliminate Butch himself.

Well, anyway, I'm thinking about all this and the judge comes in and now the prosecutor is ready to turn me over to the other lawyer. He's asked me a few more minor questions, nothing to speak of, and he says to the other lawyer, 'Your witness.' And the first one of the defense lawyers gets up and, 'Your name is Johnny Forza, huh?'

'Uh-huh.'

'You come from Brooklyn?'

'I used to.' I'm trying to be calm. He's starting out calm. Then, all of a sudden, he explodes: 'Are you the same Johnny Forza that was under investigation and picked up and arraigned five years ago on suspicion of murder?'

'But, I beat that . . .' I'm saying and starting to explain.

'Just answer yes or no! Are you the same one?'

'Ah, yeah, I'm the same one.'

'Are you the same Johnny Forza that was arrested for assault and battery last year?'

'Yeah, well, I mean there was a . . .'

'Answer yes or no!' And he's starting to scream at me. He's coming on strong and he's trying to make me feel like, hey, ain't I got nothing to say in this whole world? That's the way they want you. Just answer yes or no because he makes his question so that no matter what you answer it's going to come out to his advantage. And he keeps pounding at me. And he turns his back on me and he's facing the jury, leaning on the railing of the jury box and he yells. 'How about the time when you were arrested on suspicion of being a drug pusher, Mister Forza?' He's not even looking at me now. He's looking at the jury with a smirk on his face, as much as to say, 'What's his answer now?' And I turn around and say, 'I was never picked up for anything like that.'

'Oh, weren't you? Wait a minute. Let me check the record on that.' And he walks over to his table. Big actor, you know? He's going to get the Oscar. And he checks the record, 'Oh, my mistake.' Meantime, it's in the minds of the jury that I'm a dope pusher and nobody can do anything about it. He's not going to apologize to me or nothing, and I can't yell at him that he said this about me and it wasn't true because there's so many things he said that were true. 'And you were caught red-handed – and carrying a loaded gun – in a warehouse with a trailer-load of stolen whiskey by the police and you went to court and you lied and said that it wasn't yours that you were just meeting somebody, you didn't even know it was there? Now did you lie at that time?'

'Yes.'

'Well, why did you lie?'

'I lied to save my own neck. That's why I lied. Doesn't everybody?'

'Your honor, you see, this witness is very sarcastic.' And he turns to the jury and asks them how they can believe anything I say because I just admitted lying. If I lied then, how do they know I'm not lying now, he asks, hammering away at me to make this jury say to themselves, 'He's a lying son-of-a-bitch.' All they know is that I am an ex-con, a liar, a thief, a probable murderer, a hi-jacker, a dope pusher, a numbers operator. I'm everything these fourteen people are supposed to despise. And this is what he wants them to know. He don't want them to know anything about his client that's sitting next to him. He wants them to forget that there is a trial for hijacking here. He wants to go to the jury box now and say, 'Hey, Mister Jury, we got a bum over here testifying against the Olive Oil King. Pillar of society, goes to church every Sunday. I'll bring a priest in to prove that my client goes to church. And a dozen character witnesses to prove that he's an upstanding man in his community.' His client ain't going to take the stand so they can rip him apart, like I'm on the stand, you understand? And they're just going to keep pounding away. I'm a liar. I'm no good. Why did I do this? How do they know I'm not lying now?

The defense lawyer walks back to his table, picks up some papers, and comes up and shows me a picture and says, 'Do you know this young lady?'

'Yeah, I know her.'

'What's her name?'

'Her name is Nancy Martin.'

'How well do you know her?' And I'm thinking, the son-of-a-bitch. What a question to ask. Of course I know her. He knows that I know her better than I know my wife and this creep is trying to make it sound dirty. He screws his secretary in the office every day and he's acting shocked.

'She's a friend of mine,' I say.

'How close a friend?'

'A good friend.'

'Isn't it true that on such and such a day you and she shared the same room in London?'

And I say, 'Yeah.' I don't remember, but I know damn well if I say that or if I say it isn't true, he has a registration card there, he's got dead reckoning of what took place. So, I says, 'Yeah, we did.'

'Well, aren't you married?'

'Yeah, I'm married.'

'Well, Mister Forza, you're a liar, a thief, and now a confessed adulterer, and you want this court to forget this and believe that – out of all the other times that you were never a good person – now you're a good person!' He's shouting at me. 'And you want us to believe that you wouldn't want to get out there now with this young lady, this tramp, and that's the reason you're doing this?'

And all I can do is say, 'Yes.' Because he knows it's the truth and he's probably got documents to prove that I was in all these places. It's as simple as that. So, he got me coming and going.

This takes about three-quarters of an hour to an hour. Okay, now this guy's the loudmouth. Then comes the soft-toned voice. Another lawyer comes up with, 'John, you feeling all right today? You look magnificent in that out-fit.' Like we're long-lost brothers or something, you know? And basically, it's the same old thing. 'We want you to tell the truth now, John.'

And I say, 'Well, I am telling the truth.'

'Well, how do we know this, John?' In a nice quiet way, sticking daggers all over me. They got three lawyers and they set up a strategy: who's going to be tail man, who's going to be front man. The Old Man's lawyer gets up first and he machine-guns me for a while. A guy that tries to outtalk you, that's a machine-gunner. And he does it until the next man gets his time to bat, and the next man.

After about an hour of swinging back and forth, the judge turns around and says to the defense and to the prosecutor, 'If you want any more questions out of this man, please ask them now, because I'm going to dismiss him otherwise.'

So the prosecutor asks a few more questions, things he might have thought up while the defense was question-ing me. He thinks that maybe I seemed a little shaky on a question and he wants to clear it up. And that gives the defense the chance to ask a few more questions. The loud-mouth lawyer turns around and says, 'Mister Forza, why are you testifying.'

And my answer is, 'Just because I want to testify.'

He says, 'Are you trying to tell me that you're just a

patriotic American and that all of a sudden, after leading a life of crime for all those years, you've decided that you can't stand the rest of the criminals in the world? That you're all of a sudden a goody-two-shoes? Or are you trying to tell me that the government promised you something?'

'No, the government didn't promise me a thing.' And that's a fact. The government never promises you nothing.

'Are you trying to sit there and let this jury and this court believe that you're up here because you're a patriotic American?'

'I'm not patriotic.'

'You say the government didn't promise you anything.'

'No.'

'Mister Forza, have you ever been in prison?'

'Yes.'

'How much time have you spent in prison?'

'I did two years . . .'

'Did you like being in prison?' He's smiling at the jury.

'No.'

'Wouldn't you do anything to keep from going back to prison? Anything?'

'Well, I . . .'

He interrupts me and yells, 'Wouldn't you lie? Wouldn't you perjure yourself? Wouldn't you say anything at all to stay out of prison?'

'No – I . . .' And I'm thinking, I guess I would say about anything, except I'm not lying.

'Isn't that the deal you made with the government? That you would come here and testify in return for a suspended sentence?'

'No, no, no.'

'Would you mind explaining why you're here, then?'

'The government told me that if I agreed to testify they would make certain recommendations to the court—'

'Recommendations!' he yells. 'Don't you mean they guaranteed you a deal? You wouldn't testify without a deal, right?'

'They didn't guarantee anything about my sentence.'

'Well, what did they promise you?'

'They also told me they'd take my wife . . .'

'That's enough! That'll do!' The defense turns his back on me and starts to walk away. 'Wait a minute,' I say. 'You asked me a question.' I turn to the judge. 'Your honor, can I answer?' And the judge says, 'You asked him to answer this question, now let him do it.'

'But your honor,' the defense is sputtering, 'It's not necessary . . .' Because he don't want me to get out what I'm going to say next. And the prosecutor asks. 'What did the government promise about your wife?'

'They told me they would take her to an undisclosed spot where she would be under protection.'

'What is she under protection for?'

'Objection.' And the judge says, 'Overruled.'

'She's under protection because the people that I'm testifying against are trying to kill me and my wife.' And all the objections in the world start popping up. I get protection from the United States government against me and my family being killed and, now, the jury looks at me like, 'Is it that serious?' Now, some guys who were sitting in that jury half-asleep are wide awake, they don't want to miss none of this. The prosecution jumps right in there, now there's a new door been opened. 'And, now, Mister Forza, would you explain to the court just why you first decided to testify?'

And I go through the whole thing. How they stole my money and informed on me and the only way for me to get even with them was to agree to tell the truth. 'Remember, you're under oath!' says the prosecutor.

'I'm telling the truth.'

'And for this the government didn't promise you anything. It did suggest that we would try and help you gain early parole, but there was no guarantee. Do you agree to this?' Now the jury, they're sitting on the edge of their pants because this thing is starting to get a little serious. There's murders being mentioned and maybe my wife is going to be shot. Okay, so before that they said I was an adulterer and a junk pusher and a murderer. That's old now. The jury figured the defense is going to say these things about me, you know?

What the defense does say is, 'Well, now that you've made a public confession that you are a thief, how do you expect this jury to believe you?'

'I don't care who believes me. I'm here telling the truth. Whoever wants to believe me, believe me. If they want to convict this man, let them convict him . . .' I got cut short three times. 'If they don't want to convict him, let them turn him loose. I couldn't care less.' And I really meant it. And the jury could see that I meant it. I wasn't trying to duck that I was telling the truth. I told the truth. I wasn't up there trying to make myself look like a hero. That's exactly what I said, 'I'm not trying to make myself look like a hero. I'm here because I'm trying to save my own neck, after the mob put it to me that they wanted to kill me and my wife.'

This is what drew attention. In the meantime, outbursts in the courtroom from all the defense attorneys : 'You're a liar. Can't you admit that you're a liar?' And I say, 'Yeah, I'm a liar. I lied in my own case. I'm not lying now.' And the judge is banging his gavel and the prosecutor is saying, 'I object!' And everybody's yelling. The judge is threatening to clear the court, and after a while it does quiet down and one of the defense guys, the lawyer with the big mouth, comes over and says real soft like, 'Now, Mister Forza, let's go back to Christmas week five years ago. Miss Nancy Martin, your good friend, spent that week in Jamaica. I wonder if you can tell us where you stayed?'

'I don't remember.'

'You don't?'

'No.'

'And,' he's holding up a paper to read, 'what about the long weekend she spent in Bermuda in the spring of that year. Do you recall that?'

'I'm not sure—'

'Well, do you or don't you?'

'No.' You see, he's getting into the time just before I met Nancy and I don't like to think about that. I know she knew other guys, but I don't want to hear about it.

'All right, Mister Forza, let me refresh your memory. Miss Martin registered at the Flamingo Hotel in Jamaica on such and such a day as Mrs Michael Carew and—'

The prosecutor is on his feet. 'I object, your—' he yells.

'—on the such and such day she checked into the Carlton Beach Hotel in Bermuda as Mrs Harvey Wolk, and—' the defense lawyer is yelling louder. He's outshouting the prosecutor.

'Wait a minute!' the prosecutor yells. 'That's irrelevant! I object.'

'Overruled,' says the judge. 'You don't have to shout at me.'

'—then,' says the defense guy, 'Mister Forza, would you care to tell me about Miss Martin's short vacations the following year in Acapulco at Las Brisas and at the Dorado Beach in San Juan?'

'I don't know nothing about that—'

'Oh, you don't?' he turns to the jury. 'Mister Forza, I think you know a lot about those trips and other trips. I think you know exactly what Miss Martin was up to—'

'Objection, irrelevant!'

'Your honor, we intend to show a relevant connection.'

'Overruled. Proceed, Mister Weiss.'

'Well, Mister Forza,' he's looking over his shoulder at me and I can feel my face steaming, 'as I said, we know what she was up to, don't we? I think she was doing it for money and you know what that makes her?'

'No! No! No! No!' I'm yelling.

'That makes her a prostitute, Mister Forza, a call girl. A woman who sells herself for money. And that makes you a—'

And I'm on my feet screaming, '—motherfucker gutterous bastard you! I'll kill you for that—' and I start down from the stand and before I've taken two steps court officers are running over and they grab my arms and hold me and I'm screaming at this shit, 'You call me a *gornuda* you prick you—' and the judge is pounding with his hammer again and telling me if I don't sit down he's going to hold me in contempt. So, I sit back down in the witness chair there.

Now, I'm mad. I ain't afraid no more. Since my temper took the best of me. They want this to happen because they're looking for me to say something that's going to make a mistrial. But on the other hand, it's to my benefit too. As long as I keep a little cool, my temper will do me a world of good. It will get this poison out of my system. When the jury sees me in a fit of temper, they'll say, 'This guy can't be lying, look at the emotion on his face.'

The Old Man is sitting there looking so angelic, like he wouldn't hurt a fly. But he's a deadly, deadly man and no one's ever going to know about it. I'm the dirty, rotten son-of-a-bitch. I turned against my so-called friends. The Old Man is not going to take the stand. As long as he don't get up there and let them ask questions, then nothing about his past record can be mentioned without it being a mistrial. So the jury will never know what this guy is until after the trial when they read about him in the papers.

I look over at Mister Oakes and he gives me a nod, as much as to say, 'You're doing great. Don't worry about it, pal.' And that gives me a little confidence, because I know that this guy's in there trying to protect me. The hell with the prosecutor – he's in there for the glory.

In the meantime, I'm still looking around the court-room trying to figure what the hell's going on, why they are staring at me so bad. What am I doing wrong? I know what I'm doing wrong, but why does the jury think I'm doing wrong? Ain't I supposed to be a hero for coming in here, risking my life, protecting the rest of the United States against this creep? As far as the jury's concerned I'm not. As far as the jury's concerned, I'm lower than lice. That's what really hurts when you go this route and you find that ordinary suckers deep down really admire wiseguys and hate squealers and stoolies. It's like every-body seen too many Cagney movies and really took it to heart.

In other words, I'm a bad guy because I'm informing against the Old Man and other people. To the jury, I'm pushing over the applecart, because to them the Old Man and the rest of them are actually heroes. They're the type that you read about as little men knocking out guys bigger than them, and secretly underneath the public wants to believe this. They want to believe that there's a certain group of people, underworld or not, that nobody can push around, you understand? Because the average person gets pushed around a lot. Back of their minds it's very romantic for them to think, 'Hey, I'd like to be like that guy, boy he never gets pushed around.' And here comes this big jerk that's going to inform on him, and people relate to that guy. They don't relate to the informer.

The informer is the weasel and not only don't the

people of the underworld like him, the police don't like him either. Because it's only common sense. I mean it, let's presume you didn't have any reason to do this except to get out of jail. Well, that just isn't the way you play the game. You went out and you made all the money illegally you could get your hands on, you allied yourself with these people, you done as bad as them and worse. Now comes time to pay the piper for playing the tune and you don't wanna pay. Understand? If you have no other reason to inform on these people except just to save your own skin, you're a weasel.

I could have done all my time standing on my left ear. I really could have. But Butch and the Old Man took the heart right out of me and I had to go against them if for no other reason than just to keep my sanity. Because they screwed me around so much that I just can't stand the thought of me rotting away in jail and them walking around outside or someone spending more money, going to bed with my girlfriend, taking over my businesses, abusing my family — all this stuff — when they have no right to even do it. Because basically, I know in my heart that I was put here by the mob. They informed on me, that's why I got to do this. Them are the kind of guys that are weasels. I should be a hero, but I'm not a hero. That is what's bothering me.

And one of the defense attorneys walks by the jury, 'I don't want to have anything to do with that man anymore. He's nothing but a damn liar.' And this is inadmissible in court. You don't know some of the things they pull; they're as cute as apples. 'We don't want anything to do with him. Get rid of him! Take him out, he's stinking up the courtroom!' Really, they get away with it. The judge is staring, won't say a word, because he figures if he says something now to protect me they could use it against him in appeal.

So the lawyers go up to the front and the judge says,

'Are you all through with him, defense?' And one of the lawyers says, 'Yes.' 'Are you all through with him, prosecution?' And when the prosecutor says he is, the judge nods to Mister Oakes and says, 'Marshals, take him out of here.' Then they take me back to that room while they make their plans to get all of them police and marshals out of the courtroom. I could just see Mister Oakes saying, 'You move around into the audience there, among the people, and see if you hear anything about what they're doing.' And I'm waiting here for Mister Oakes when the prosecutor comes charging in. He's white in the face. 'Forza! Goddammit! Why did you let him get to you?' He's shaking.

'You wouldn't understand,' I tell him. 'There's some things you just can't take. If a friend had said that to me in Sicilian, I'd have had to kill him or I'm not a man. I'm sorry I blew, but I really couldn't help it.'

'Well,' says the prosecutor, 'they knew what they were doing with you. They wanted you to blow and lose the case. And maybe they're going to get what they wanted.'

I'm trying to defend what I did. 'Listen, why did the judge let that guy say all those things? It had nothing to do with the case.'

'The judge is afraid of a mistrial, so he leans over backwards, he leans over so far he's lying down to avoid giving them an excuse for that. He gives the defense every break and then a few more.' And the prosecutor gives me a little smile and a slap on the back and walks out.

Down in the courtyard in back, a bunch of police cars and a van are gunning their engines. And the gates open and four, five cars tear out with the van, sirens screaming. They stop traffic and everybody's chasing them and taxicabs are making noise with their horns. A real mess. And about seven minutes later Mister Oakes and I, just the way we are, walk out, get in his car, drive down the street, take a left nice and quiet, no one protecting us, just him and I mosey out and away.

So that's what a man like me faces when he goes into that room. As tough and big as I'm supposed to be, when I got in there my legs are watery and I'm wobbly and my spine feels like jelly all of a sudden – because I'm doing something I been taught since age one never to do: *talk*. You understand? This was the most important thing in my life. You can't talk. You can't talk. Now, I'm being told : talk to save your life. So to save my life, I'm talking. And the meantime, I'm putting myself in danger. And the point is, how are they going to take care of me?

# CHAPTER THREE

Every night and every day since I've gone with the government, one main fear is that Butch has been sent to find me, cause he *will* find me – he has the patience of a saint. And he'll love what he has to do to me. He knows where I got my money hidden, where my girlfriend is, where my mother is, the kind of food I like to eat, what I like to drink, what I like to do in bed. The real worry is trying to remember what I told Butch during all those years we spent together. How much does he know? What things will he remember?

I'm thinking about one time when we were loan-sharking. It's things like this that come back to me, see, and make me fear him more than anybody. We'd loaned money to a cab driver, pretty tough kid, too, and he owed us $20,000. He couldn't pay and Butch went over to collect and in the scuffle he got the worst of it. And this kid knew he was a dead man after that, so he ran away. The guy's friends said he told them he was going to Hawaii. And then Butch remembered drinking with this guy once and him saying he'd spent time in the army at Fort Benning and still had the hots for some girl he'd known in Columbus, Georgia. So, before going to Honolulu, Butch checks with one of his guys who was boffing a tomato who worked in the U.S. Health and Welfare Department, Social Security office, and she took this clown's number and checked the computer and found he'd been on a payroll of a cab company in Honolulu for a month or so, but a new employer in Atlanta had just sent his number in.

So Butch and another fella went down there and inves-

72

tigated a little bit and the guy happened to be off the day they got there, and they found out he lived in a trailer camp about forty miles outside of Atlanta. They went out there and caught him at midnight. And after the scuffle this time Butch didn't get the worst of it. We got our money because he made the guy sell the trailer the next day. It was all paid for.

My point is that once someone bruises this kid or pushes him around or gets the best of him, he will never forget. Revenge, revenge, revenge, that's all he thinks of. Well, maybe that's good. I used to be like that, but then I got a little bit of compassion, you know, after I made it and I knew I didn't have to get up and fight every morning. I'd wake up and I had my day's pay made and I guess I got a little soft. But Butch never did. He's more of an animal than ever. Better dressed now, but still an animal. And now you see how I know that if anyone gets me, Butch will be responsible, if not directly, indirectly. As a friend you couldn't put Butch down. He'd put his life on the line for you. When he would go to a new tailor he'd have some shirts made, and I could always count on half a dozen or a dozen that he would have made for me when he was my friend. And I'd be very honored. But the point is, he wasn't always a friend. And now, he's a deadly enemy.

Butch is an enemy that won't give up – ever. He'll try everything and anything and he knows a lot to try. He might even get me through the social-security thing. Butch found that connection so good he's got a guy in the bag at the computer center in Baltimore. They are very, very tight about giving out where anyone works. They ain't even supposed to tell the cops or the FBI. Even if you're the wife of a guy who run out, the only thing they do is send a letter for you to where they have him down as working last. They don't tell you where that is and if he don't answer the letter you never find out. This guy in

73

Baltimore was like gold to us and we used him only for hard-to-find lamsters. Of course, Butch knows I know about this deal, and if I ever go to work I'll have a new social-security number in a new name. But there's more to it than that. You know, the marshals got me a number under my new name, but I know that if you just change your name they give you the old number, or they give you a new one and move the records from the old one to the new one. Understand? So I told them I got to have a real new number and forget the money credited to me in my old account. I'm never going to collect on it anyhow. Even so, I know I'm not safe from Butch and his computer man. Trouble is there aren't that many guys around age forty-five with Italian names who never had a social-security card before, with a new one that was issued like six months ago. Thousands, maybe, but Butch and his man in Baltimore could cut it down pretty quick. If I ever give my new number to anyone who winds up sending it to the Social Security I'll be done. And they're always sending for the number, like for a driver's license, a bank account, a library card, insurance, a tax return, a charge account. Everybody wants that damn number.

I been in this goddamn car now for three hours with these two high-muckymuck marshals here. They're driving me to Washington but they're acting cold towards me. If I hadn't seen these two before I'd think I was being taken for a ride. I'd like to know what the hell the story is. Did I do something wrong? They're acting just like the jury did. I ask them a question and they don't even answer. I know damn good and well this trip that they're taking me down to Washington for one of two reasons – either they're going to want me to testify some more and keep me under protection, or they're turning me over to the wolves and cutting me loose. Look at the marshal in the front seat smoking a pipe. You can't trust a damn pipe-

74

smoker. Old Don Mario used to say that all the time. You can't take a look at their eyes with all that smoke in front of them.

'Well,' I ask the guy with the pipe, 'Bill, where are you taking me? What's going on?'

He tells me, 'Mister Forza,' and that's when I start worrying, when he calls me Mister Forza. 'Mister Forza,' he says, 'we have instructions to bring you down here and we can't say any more to you than that. Don't get mad at us, we're only doing our job. Everything's going to work out for you, don't worry about it.'

Well, I think he's throwing the bullshit. He knows exactly what's going on and he's just been instructed to keep his mouth shut so they can drop the bomb on me all at once. The other marshal's telling me the same thing: 'Take it easy. You'll be all right, Mister Forza. Don't worry. Pretty soon you're going to be a free man.'

That's the first thing that's happened when I can really say they let something out of the bag. They're going to cut me loose, no question about it. I can see it in their eyes. They look at me and say to themselves, 'You stupid bastard. We used you, you got a little money out of us, you got a little free time out of us, now you're going to be on your own, mister, and we can go home and do a little golfing and go fishing with the kids and we could care less.' The next day they might read in the paper that Johnny Forza gets whacked in the head. They're going to say, 'Well, sorry about that. He wasn't a bad fella.' And that's going to be the only comment.

Now we're pulling off the highway and onto a street. I don't know where the hell we are. Last time, I came here by helicopter and we landed at some fort on the river and drove off in an Army car. We go through a long park with high walls and trees on both sides. Not many cars. Great for an ambush. And now we're downtown in a high-class shopping area and as always there's construction

75

going on, jackhammers, drills, and this and that. It's hard to hear through the digging up things.

Here we are, we're pulling up on Twelfth Street to the old Safeway International Building where the marshals got their headquarters. They got a huge supermarket on the ground floor there where all the people from the embassies go, and they carry stuff for the Indian people like curry and lamb, and you see all the diplomats with chauffeurs going in there. And we park in a lot across the street and walk over to the building. We take the unmarked entrance to the left of the supermarket. There's a revolving door into a little lobby with marble floors and a black guy dressed in a government police uniform. The marshals identify themselves and he looks at the time and says, 'Okay, it's one-ten' and we all sign the book. There's three elevators in front of us and we take the one on the right, and there's a camera outside the door and inside there's another television camera putting the nod on you so that they know who's coming up. And we go up to the third floor and get out of the elevator and there's cameras all over the goddamn place – one every ten feet. A lot of black secretaries are walking around and guys smoking pipes. They're forever smoking pipes. Guys standing near the water cooler and everybody with a gun on and a badge, you know, in plain clothes –very, very cold-looking.

And now we're on our way to the office of Mister Francis, the man that does the hatchet-chopping. I been in here a couple of times before. When I first went with the government, I was taken up to this Francis's office and he gave me the layout of the track and which way things had to be done and so forth. And, as you walk off the elevator, you walk down a corridor and on the wall there's a plaque of the United States Marshal Service Badge, and you finally get to the door and you stand there for a minute. Then all of a sudden the buzzer goes and the door opens up and they let me in. We walk into the office and there's a secretary there and a marshal leans out and says, 'I want to see Mister Francis. I have Mister Forza here with me.' So she picks up the phone and she says, 'Marshal Clemson is here with Mister Forza,' and she hangs up and tells us, 'Wait a few minutes, he's on the phone.'

So we sit down. The sweat is starting to pour off me, see, and this is raw nerves. What is he making me sit here for? He didn't make me sit here the first time I came in here. No sir, the first time I went in those goddamn doors, the son-of-a-bitch walked me right into his office, didn't even bother with the secretary. But now they're all through squeezing the orange, all they want to do is push me out, the bastards. After about fifteen minutes, the secretary's phone rings. She picks it up and she says, 'Yes,' sir.' She hangs up and she tells the marshals, 'Bring him into room seven.' We walk in and there's about a fifteen-foot-long table with maybe fourteen chairs around it. In back of the head of the table is a picture of the President and a flag of the United States Marshals and a flag of the United States and a picture of the director of the Marshals, Wayne Colburn, and a few other pictures in there showing different centers and judges and all this. And they sit me down and all of a sudden I start getting a pain in my stomach and I know it's going to be bad.

So far not one of these bastards has even offered me a cup of coffee. They couldn't do enough for me when I was in here before: 'Hi, Johnny, can we get you some coffee? How about a sandwich? A glass of milk? A cold drink? Water? Soda? Want to take my wife out?' Anything, they didn't give a shit. Now they offer me nothing. And these two marshals aren't sitting down, they're standing behind me, which makes me think of guys who got it in the back – knife, a gun, a rope. I start to get up and they tell me to sit down, and I say, 'Remember now, I'm a free man. I'm on parole.' They're expecting their boss in here and when he walks in they want to make it look good. Bastards! Boy, would I love to get up and just smash their heads in and run out of here.

I almost wish this was a parole hearing. At least I'd know how it would go. I'd be standing in front of a table like this with seven or eight guys and a woman sitting around and a foreman at the top of the table there. They ask me my name and what I was sentenced for and then a lot of foolish questions like how do you feel about society and how do you feel towards your mother now? All this bullshit. They want to see if you're mentally able to go out and combat the world. Actually, half the time it's a lot of malarky. If someone's got to them you get out. If they didn't you don't, and that's the end of it.

The door opens and here he comes, Old Fancy Pants, Mister Francis. Here's the guy that turns in his own boss and gets him fired from the service so he can take his job. The dirty, rotten creep. I say, 'Hi, Mister Francis. How are you?'

'Fine, thank you.' And he walks right by and goes to the head of the table. He's got a folder with him and he puts it down in front of him and sits down. I hate the son-of-a-bitch's guts with a passion. He's got a pair of striped pants on that went out with Genghis Khan for chrissake, they're so old and shiny, too. Well, this is what I've dreamt of. I'm in his hands and there's not a damn thing I can do about it. I'm looking him in the eye, and I'm trying to figure what he has in mind. 'You bastard, what are you reading?' is running through my mind. He hasn't said a word.

After what seems like about an hour, this clown that looks like he takes logs up the ass, looks up from his papers and he's got a smirk on his face. 'You know, Forza,' he says, 'I think it's about time we said goodbye. We're terminating you.' He catches me off guard there for a minute with the word terminating. Termination. That means you're going to shoot me? Or you're going to just cut me loose? I says to him, 'What does that mean?'

'What we're going to do is give you your freedom. We're going to give you a ticket and we're going to turn you loose. You're on your own.' He's grinning at me.

'What do you mean, I'm on my own? What if I need help from the marshals? What if I have to call you – not that I want to, you rotten bastards!'

'Don't talk to me that way,' he says.

'I'll talk to you any way I want,' I'm yelling. 'Now, you just told me I'm a free man. What if I need you, will you come?'

'Well, we'll see. You can give us a call and we'll think it over.'

I said, 'By the time you're thinking it over, they'll cut me up for bacon. You son-of-a-bitch, you wanted this all the time. You look down on me like I'm dirt.'

'You are dirt, Forza.' He stands up and points his finger at me. 'You're scum and we were dumb to trust you to do what you promised. You blew the case against your old pal Scordato. The jury turned him loose this morning.'

'What do you mean, I blew the case? I told the truth. I said everything that was asked. I—'

'You know what I mean, Forza. You couldn't hold your temper and you didn't try. You blew the case and I think you did it on purpose.'

And I'm sputtering, 'You bastard—' At the same time, I'm thinking, did I know what I was doing when I got mad at that defense lawyer? Did I really blow up to save the Old Man? I don't think I did, but this jerk's got under my skin. And, he's saying 'I wonder how much they're paying you. If it was up to me I'd send you back to Lewisburg on the next train.'

'Paying me? Why you no good son-of-a-bitch, I'll—' and I start to get up and grab him by the throat and I feel

79

myself pushed down hard in the chair. It's the marshals standing behind me.

'Listen, we don't want any trouble with you. Just get out of here. The men'll take you to where you have to be taken. I told you, you're on your own as of now. You're never getting any more money from us. You guys that come with the government think you're big shots because you testify against a few of your own people, your own kind. Now, go out and face them, you shit.' That's what he says to me.

I says, 'You half-fag. I'll screw your old lady in the mouth for two dollars!'

'You get out of here!' He's yelling at me and I'm yelling back and he says, 'One more word out of you and you're going to be in violation of your parole. Now get out of here!'

What else can I do? I tell him, 'Put your gun down, let me take you out in the back yard and knock your brains out. Who the hell do you think you're talking to?' The other two marshals are pulling me by the shoulders. 'Come on, get out of here, Forza, before you get yourself in trouble.' But right now, I don't give a shit if I do or not. Then Francis says to me, 'Here, you have to sign the release,' and he hands me this paper.

I throw it back at him. 'Stick it up your ass, you son-of-a-bitch! You sign it.'

'If you don't sign, you don't get this check.' He waves it at me. Well, at that moment, I have to count on using my head a little bit. This check is only for a few hundred dollars, but now it looks like a million to me, so I sign the goddamn paper releasing the government from all claims. If anything happens to me I am on my own and that's it. I'm on my own. What a lonely feeling. Wow. Where do I go now? What do I do now? So I give the paper back to him and say, 'You know, if you do this to me, you'll never get anyone else to come over and testify for the government.'

And he just looks at me for a minute and says, 'I never liked the idea of using you guys anyway. It's a disgrace to the country to bargain with gangsters. It makes my sense of justice cringe that the government offered you a deal.' He says, 'Get him out of here.' And that's that.

We leave the same way we came in. Everybody's saying, 'See you later, Johnny. See you later.' All the secretaries that I had met before. Right now, I can't even hear them. I'm numb. And now, we're getting into the damn car again. Why do I have to go with them at all? Why don't they just cut me loose right here? Throw me out of the car like a stray dog? One guy says to me, 'Look, it's not as bad as you think. Mister Oakes told us to tell you that if you have any problems you got his home number. Give him a call, we'll do everything we can to help you. We can only go so far without the boss's okay.'

'Well, where are you taking me now?'

'We're going to take you to the airport, National Airport. There's a ticket in that other envelope for you.'

I'm so frigging mad right now. Why did the son-of-a-bitch do it to me? I at least expected him to say to me, 'Look, you just finished with this case, go on home. We're going to keep in touch with you for another month and give you a chance to get on your feet. Forget the money, it isn't that important.' It's just the idea to know that someone is in my corner. I wasn't worried that they would say, 'Geez, you're the greatest guy in the world because you done these things,' but this isn't right. The government shouldn't do this to me.

Well, we're passing the Lincoln Memorial now, and we speed over the bridge and around, and I look back across the river and I see Washington all lit up, the monument and everything. And I'm saying to myself, 'Take a good

81

look, it'll probably be your last.' And it leaves me kind of sad. The car stops at the terminal building and I get out and take that old suitcase they're giving me and I say, 'You guys bringing me in?'

'No, you're on your own, John. Just be careful, try to keep a low profile.'

What a stupid thing to say. Well, I can't let them know that I'm so scared inside I'm ready to have a diarrhea attack. I shake their hands and say, 'Thanks a lot, boys. I know it wasn't your fault,' and I'm thinking all the time, 'You bastards, you're all the same.'

'Let us know if you move,' they say. 'Keep in touch.'

'Huh,' I'm saying to myself. 'Keep in touch with what? The electric light bulb? Should I stick my finger in the socket? Maybe I'll get reconnected. What the hell am I going to do? I'm stuck at National Airport with a ticket, about thirty-five bucks in cash and a check for a lousy few hundred more. Is this all my life is?' And I walk inside. Slow, like I'm walking into a dark alley. I feel like I ought to be touching the wall and I start looking carefully, very, very carefully at people to see if they recognize me. I try not to stare at their faces, but every guy that looks at me makes me feel like he's made me. I need to get a pair of mirror shades so they won't see me looking. All these people around, running here and there. Maybe this guy's from Brooklyn and maybe that guy's from New Jersey. Suddenly, I'm feeling very scared to be unprotected in this place. It's like the yard back at the joint, with all these guys walking around and no one watches for trouble. I could get shanked and they don't see a thing. They'd think it's a heart attack. I don't want to show this but I'm feeling like I was standing naked in the middle of a highway with cars coming down on me from every which way. I'm going to get hit and I don't know where to go.

But I got to stop this before I do something dumb. I got

to settle down and think on what I'm going to do. So I walk over to the snack bar and find a place against the wall and get a cup of coffee and a sweet roll. And I'm standing here holding a newspaper in front of my face and trying to figure out what Butch knows and what he don't know and what he's done and what he's going to do. I figure it this way : Butch knows that I got out of the court-house okay and he's got to figure I went back home to where we been relocated or I went somewhere with the marshals. Now, he knows the government's going to blame me for blowing the case and that I'll get put down or at least chewed out for it. And he knows that the Witness Protection people are down here, so he knows I got to be in Washington. Butch knows a lot about their program because there's been a few guys turned before. We had to try and whack them out and in a couple cases we did. We found the government don't protect them forever, and guys slip back into old habits and places.

Actually, if the truth be known, I don't think that Butch would expect the government to terminate me like this, just dump me in the open. He'd think – like I would in his place – that they would smuggle me out of town, keep me hidden, maybe do it by helicopter. But I can't count on that. I have to think the Washington airport is definitely covered. If he was sure I was coming here he'd have it covered so heavy that I couldn't even get through. But because he's not sure, the only way would be the way he's probably done it. He's had his men tell some people, 'We're looking for him so keep an eye out for him because we want to speak to him about something.' Maybe it's the broad behind the ticket counter or one of the skycaps that picks up the baggage, someone who can say that I was there and took such-and-such a plane. I know Butch has got people looking for me that are on the payroll – railroad dicks, private eyes, airport security people. You got to understand, Butch is like a four-star general directing a goddamn army of intelligence people to catch a spy. Every day one more door closes in my face, one more exit that I can escape through closes.

So, where does that leave me? I think I know how Butch is covering this place. Now I got to figure what he thinks I'm going to do about it. He's got to know I'm going to be looking for his people and that I maybe look different from what I did in court. So, he's not going to have anybody here that I ever seen but all of them will have pictures of me to look at and maybe pictures showing me with and without a beard and bushy hair like them drawings that were on the TV. And he will know I'll expect exactly that and I'm going to be damn careful about leaving the airport so they won't know where I went. I don't think they'll try anything right here in the airport; they'll just follow me. But – I'm not sure about that. Butch maybe figures that's just what I'm thinking he'd do – so he does something else to catch me off guard. I just can't make any mistakes with this bastard. He's got all the power on his side, but I got smarts, and being alone I can move fast.

You know it's good to be on your own. I always was on my own. But this is a different situation. I was always with the good guys, at least I thought they were. Now I'm with nobody. I'm not with the bad guys, I'm not with the good guys. I'm not with anybody. I'm with myself. In a way, I'm glad. There's nobody hampering me. Wherever I want to go, I can go. What a dumb thing to say – I'm about as free as a guy in the can who finds the front gate open and when he runs out they shoot him in the back.

I open the envelope to look at my ticket and – shit! It's not a ticket, it's a long green government travel voucher. I can turn it in for a one-way ticket to Phoenix. I can't cash it or change it. Not only that, the fucking thing's made out to Frank Carpi, the name I was given when they relocated us out West. No way this was a mistake. That bastard Francis wants Butch to get me. Any ticket girl is going to remember the guy with the Italian name who comes up with a travel order instead of cash or a credit card. And after I use it to get a ticket, she's going to have that green card sitting there in the pile of ticket stubs and anyone who comes along is going to find it easy to get my new name and location. This thing means that I got to go to my old lady and take a chance that Butch catches up with me or I got to get the hell out of here in another direction and take a chance the law comes after me for violating my parole. And now I look at the check Francis gave me. Sure enough, it's also made out to Carpi. They're not taking any chances on me slipping out of the net. But I'm thinking maybe I'll just get a ticket to Phoenix and forget about it. Miss the plane, go to another airline and tell them I want to go to Denver or someplace and I'll pay the difference when I get out there. Might work. But that still leaves me with the problem of getting a plane out of here without being followed and whacked at the other end.

I don't know what to do, to tell you the truth. I'm just sitting here looking like a goddamn donkey. I know I got to think on all this, so I go in the men's room and have a smoke. Every time I've walked into a men's room in my life the first thing I do is look underneath the sitdown toilets, to see if there's anybody standing or sitting in them so I can feel comfortable when I go up against the urinator there with my back to the toilets. So, I look underneath as usual and I'm in there alone and some guy walks in. But instead of going right to either the place where you sit down or the urinator, he stands there and lights a cigarette, fools around at the sink. And all the time my suspicions are rising and rising because I'm saying to myself, 'He's figuring out if there's anybody else in here, anybody's going to come in, and how am I going to defend myself if he's got a gun or a knife?' I look at the wastebasket and I grab a hold of that for a minute just to see if it's movable so that I could try and use it to protect myself. And it all goes through my mind, 'How did I get into this mess that I got to be in a shithouse looking to get knocked off by some con I never seen before in my life?' Now, I get a sigh of relief when someone else walks in. I immediately wipe my hands and walk out fast. As I look back I see that the guy that worried me is still there, smoking and looking at himself in the mirror. And I think maybe he's just a fag who was waiting for me to make a move.

Now, right outside the men's room, a guy bumps into me and mumbles something and goes inside. I stop and feel all my pockets. Either the guy took something he could use to identify me or he slipped something into my pocket, like a knife, that would get me arrested when I walk through the X-ray machine. I don't find anything and now I'm starting to wonder if maybe the guy was trying to get a closer look at me because my hair's been dyed gray and the beard that I had in court is gone. They'll want to hear my voice, so I figure if someone comes up to me asking where the men's room is or some such, I'd probably walk away from him without answering. I'm sure Butch has got tape recordings of my voice. He loved to collect information on people. I know that he's got pictures of me and he probably got copies of the sketches made of me on the witness stand. You know, we had a way of using that stuff just like the FBI when we was looking for a guy. Butch would put together a regular yellow sheet like cops do, with prints and picture and record and description and a lot more – the food he likes, the kind of car, clothes, drinks, games, girls, the works. And we could give a sheet like that to guys who'd never seen the one we were after and right off they knew a lot about him.

But I'm thinking I could mess things up for Butch if I just change my face into something different from any of his pictures. I got no disguise kit like we used to have, but there's a little drugstore over there. So I go buy some cotton balls, hair tonic, talcum, a comb, and a little mirror. Back to the men's room – the guy's gone, thank God. I put a dime in one of the toilets there, get inside, and close the door. I start with the hair, rub a lot of oil on it and part on the side instead of combing back. Then I put talcum around the sides until they're near white. Comb the eyebrows up bushy. And I stuff my mouth full of cotton balls, push 'em back on both sides 'til I can't get no more in without choking. Feels shitty but it makes me look round-faced, maybe even changes my talk. I check the mirror one more time. Not bad. I'm fatter and older. I get up to leave and I'm coming to the tough part – the way I walk, you know, the wiseguy strut, coming on like you own the place. It's hard to stop, and like I said, it's the easiest thing in the world for another wiseguy, not just a head-hunter, to spot. I got to remember not to walk the way I always walk, so I put a quarter in the heel of each shoe. Don't hurt, but reminds me I got to walk different, slouch, stroll like a sucker. It's hard. It even makes me feel bad.

I go down to the counter where the girls are and say, 'I need a ticket for Phoenix, Arizona, and here's my voucher. Economy class.' And when I tell her that, my voice is thick like I got a mouth full of dry bread and I have to talk slow. She makes out the ticket and I laugh and joke with her a bit. You know, bullshit with her about how pretty she is and the weather and all. In the meantime, I'm looking all over the damn terminal there to see if anybody is looking at me with fish eyes. Girls are always picking up phones, calling in to a dispatcher or something, and every time one of them picks up the phone my head is snapping around to see, my ears straining to hear what they have to say, since maybe one of them is calling somebody on me right now. The most important thing for me to do is to get past the X-ray machine. Once I get inside there I figure I got it made, I mean as far as living for a couple more hours. I'm not going to get blasted down in the middle of the lobby there, but if the wiseguys have guns they could take me in a corner, whack me in the head, and two of them carry me out, making out like I'm drunk or something. A cop sees them and one says, 'Had a little too much to drink, you know.' And the cop says, 'Yeah, well don't let him lay around here. Need some help, fellas?' Or, one of them's a security guard or detective with a license to have a piece in his hand. You see, Butch knows I haven't got a gun. The marshals would have never let me near one and I had no chance to buy or steal one. And he'll figure even if I had, I'd be scared to have it on me for fear of getting collared with it. But Butch also knows that lamsters get desperate when they're being tracked. The longer I'm loose the more he's got to assume I got a gun on me. Won't really make no difference, he just puts tougher monkeys on me.

Here I am alone after two-and-a-half years of either being in a cell or in a hotel room surrounded by guys with guns. Whether they were smarter or not, they were still guys with guns and they might scare other people away. Now I'm walking in a crowd up a small ramp into American Airlines' area. Lot of people scurrying around, and I got to tell you something: I feel awful lonely. I'm not used to traveling alone – not that I'm looking for companionship. I just wish I had a thirty-eight. At least it'd give me something, some way to even up the score, to make me feel better.

All of a sudden, out of the corner of my eye, I catch a guy that looks around quick and then decides to get out of line all of a sudden. I figure he must have been spotting me and didn't realize what he was doing when he got in this line. He must have a piece on him, and he's going to run and drop a dime to where I'm going through, maybe duck the gun in one of those airport lockers, and come back through to see exactly what I'm up to. So, I go through the machine. I still got my suitcase with me. They send it through the X-ray machine and out it comes on the other side. I pick it up. I feel a little bit relieved now. I could fight anyone with my hands that I need to. At least I know the son-of-a-bitch ain't going to have a gun.

And, the guy does follow me down there, because about seven or eight minutes after I go through, sure enough here comes this guy. And I'm keeping my eyes on the passengers that are passing through here and I have to walk down to Gate 16. At the gate, after I'm there a few minutes, here comes this guy again. He is definitely following me. Does he have a ticket to go with me on the same plane? That's what I have to worry about. It could be a completely innocent thing. He maybe forgot to get his ticket validated or maybe he wanted to buy a magazine at the corner outside. But I have to presume the worst. I can't say, 'Well, he's a preacher.' I got to say, 'He's a killer.' Has Butch told this guy to go the route with me no matter where I go? Stay on even if it's obvious? Sweat me a little?

Now, how the Christ am I going to get out of this airport without being spotted? I'd like to call Nancy up, but I'm sure Butch has got her covered. What do I do? Get on the plane and go back there and try and hide for a while, or make a break right now? If they know what plane I'm on they'll have the airport in Phoenix covered and it'll be harder to get out of than this one – not so many people to get lost in. So I better try it right here. But how? I'm sitting here thinking and then all of a sudden I notice a crowd going to get on that plane I'm supposed to take, and that's where I head.

There's a bunch of people in front of me where you show your ticket to the guy and I'm standing there wondering who they got around here following me. I don't see the guy who dropped out of the X-ray line any-more, but there's a porter over there who looks like he's spotting me. Is he the one? I'm sure they got somebody here. I'm past the ticket taker now and standing in a crowd waiting for them to let us get on the plane. And I give a fast look back and – son-of-a-bitch – Mister Oakes is over there across the hall and he's waving at me. I swear to God it's him and I'm caught here in this mob and I can't do nothing but wave back and I almost trip over my suitcase with someone pushing and I look back and Mister Oakes is gone like a shadow. Now, I'm wondering if I really saw him or not. It could have been someone who looks like him who was waving to a friend. I know he's not on duty today: I asked them in Washington. But, you know, I think it was Mister Oakes there and he watching to see that nothing happened to me and waving at me as much as to say, 'Don't worry, Johnny.' I hope it was Mister Oakes. I pick up my suitcase and I head out very slow into the walkway to the airplane. I feel the hairs on the back of my neck going up because I'm sure some-one else's watching me get on this plane, and I'm saying to myself, 'Bastard, as soon as I get off of this thing I hope you run and drop a dime that I'm on a flight for Dallas, El Paso, and Phoenix. That'll give them three locations to figure out where I'm going. Butch is not dumb either. He'll alert people in them areas to keep an eye for what time the plane is supposed to land in all three cities, but in the back of his mind he's saying, 'It's too obvious. Johnny Forza ain't that stupid. He wouldn't just get on a plane knowing that more than likely we have someone spotting the area.' So if he's getting the word right now that I'm on that plane he's not going to believe it, and he's going to tell the boys to check out the airport and check it good.

I'm getting near the turn in the walkway, hanging back there so there's not too many people behind me and a mob in front. I move to one side to let a couple get by. Funny how they're always in a hurry to get in and sit down and wait, like maybe there won't be enough seats. Around the turn and the people are moving slow as the girls look at each ticket and make with the big smile and hello. The door to the plane is about ten feet in front of me and the walkway is wider there and the people are really a mob, nudging and pushing. On the right side of the walkway, just as it gets wider, is a little narrow door, metal with a plastic window in it like an aluminum storm door. I move over to it and let a couple of other people get past me, and I drop my newspaper and bend down to pick it up, like it's hard for me to move. And I'm looking up sideways as I reach down for the paper. Everybody's facing towards the plane; I see only their backs. Without standing up, I reach over, grab the door handle, turn it and slip through quick. I'm on a little metal platform outside the walkway and it's dark, and if anyone gets in my way I'm going to slam 'em. I go down some narrow metal stairs and I'm on the cement under the plane. I don't think anybody even seen me go. Twenty feet away guys are loading baggage under a light, so I duck under the walkway where it's dark and start walking back to the terminal just like I know what I'm up to.

The whole area is busy as hell, loaded with mechanics and guards and guys in white coveralls. There's a couple of big lights but you can't see anybody's face clear. I'm walking fast and nobody gives me a look. They figure anybody out there must have a reason, and I got a reason, all right. I get to the wall of the building and pass a couple of doors with no lights and some dark windows and then a door marked 'Keep Out. American Airlines. Employees Only'. I open the door and go right in just like I owned the joint. It's a locker room for mechanics or whatever, and I look around fast and try a few of the lockers to see what I can find. First one is empty, next four are locked and then I hit one that's open and has coveralls, tools, and a white crash helmet in it – you know, them helmets the guys wear out on the cement. And I'm pulling the coveralls on over my suit when the door opens and a guy comes in and asks, 'Hey, who're you? What are you doing in here?' I don't answer him. I zip up the coveralls and I'm walking by him to the door when he grabs hold of my arm. Smash! Right in the face with the damn suitcase. He goes down and a couple of kicks to his head and balls and he's out. Now I grab his wallet and take his money and I unclip his ID card from the front of his coveralls. I went this far, I might as well go all the way now. I've done an assault on this guy which means a bit for me if I get caught, and a bit for me means death. So I give him a few more kicks to make sure he's out for a while.

I get out of the locker room and find a baggage tug outside that this guy had been driving. They look like a golf cart, only they pull a train of baggage cars. I put my suitcase in one of the cars and get in the driver's seat, and wonder where to drive. This thing probably works like a forklift, like they use on the docks and in warehouses. Not much faster than a walk, but a way to get out of here with nobody looking. And the guy left keys in it. I push out the clutch, put it in gear, ease in, and it jerks and quits on me.

Christ! I better get this thing started and away or get the hell off it. Some guy's going to wonder what's wrong and come over to help, and that's all. Or another guy's going to come on shift and he walks in the locker room and all hell breaks loose when he sees that jerk on the floor there. I give it another try and this time let the clutch in very slow – and it catches and I hit the gas and she dies again. Now, I'm really sweating, but I know what the hell's wrong and I hate to let this goddamn thing get away from me. So, I do it again – and she catches and we're off and nobody's looking yet. I start this buggy down to the right and I'm picking my way between trucks and planes and it's not easy with five cars trailing you. And I'm passing a guy who looks like a private cop and he waves and says something. I wave back and yell, 'Hello,' hoping he's not looking for some other answer. I figure I can go down to the end of the terminal building and right out the gate and leave this thing and grab a cab.

And then I see the police car parked there, and I know they'll never let me through. Since the mob started hijacking stuff from airports, they all put in tight security. And I'm thinking it would be a riot if one of these truckdrivers really is a wiseguy. Anyway, I pull out in a big circle, just like I was planning to do that, and stop at the first 'Employees Only' door I come to, which is Eastern Airlines. I get down, take my bag, open the door, and step in – and it's too late to back out now. The place is lit up and there's a couple guys sitting in the corner playing cards. I just got to bluff it. So I walk right in and over to the other door, the one that leads out to the terminal, and I don't look at them, I just stagger a little and knock my suitcase against a locker and fumble with the door going out. They take me for a drunk screwing off on the job.

Outside, I'm in the Eastern Airlines shuttle area, and I go into the nearest men's room. This one is crowded and it stinks, but I don't have to check it out. With all these pissers here it's safe. I come up with a dime for the toilet and inside there I strip off the coveralls and I'm looking for a place to stash them and I wind up stuffing them inside my case. Now, I'm dressed like I was and I get rid of the damn cotton in my mouth down the toilet. I can't stand it no more and I'm afraid I'm going to choke on it like I almost did just now when I yelled at that guard. So, I check my face in the mirror on the way out and I don't look so fat. Then I see a pair of glasses in a case on the shelf under the mirror I'm using and I wash my hands again and mess with my tie and I'm looking around to see if anyone's picking them up and they don't, so I put them on and shove the case in my pocket. I can't see out of them too good, but a good disguise – a gift from God.

And I just walk upstairs, it's as simple as that. You can walk from the airfield straight upstairs to the main building. Now, I'm walking around the Eastern section and no one knows I'm here, at least I don't think they do yet. Even when they find this guy all banged up in the locker room they'll have no idea which way I went until they find the baggage cart. By that time I'll be long gone. Well, the reason why I drove down to the Eastern Airlines area is that the shuttle is there and it's crowded all the time, not just at flight time. Now, I have to presume that they got the place spotted because it's got something to do with New York, but on the other hand I feel as though I stand maybe a thirty percent better chance in that terminal than I would in American, because they'd think I'd go back to New York by myself.

I'm figuring it this way. The next thing I want is my stash, but Butch knows this as well as I do and he's going to cover the bank in New York like flypaper. He'll bet that I don't go for the stash now, but lie low and wait for him to get tired of watching it close. He checks the Boston shuttle, the other quick way out of here, and the trains and buses. He knows I got no credit cards and can't rent a car and probably won't take a chance and steal one. So he tries to figure where I might have friends he don't know about, like maybe Norfolk, Harrisburg, Scranton, Allentown. He knows I used to have people in Baltimore and we both got friends in Philadelphia, so he's got to go down the list and figure who I know that might owe me or like me enough to hold out a hand. I bet he spends the night on the phone. Maybe he even worries that I got another stash he don't know about. I don't, but he can't be sure of that. Right now, I'm sure he's trying to remember everything

I ever said about banks, and he'll have Nancy's mailbox watched to find out what bank she uses and he covers that one just in case. Same with my mother and my sister. He won't miss a trick, the bastard. But the more places he has to cover, the better for me.

So I get upstairs there and I look around and I don't feel too secure. My next sweat is when I have to walk out of there and decide which way I'm going to go. Maybe I should surprise them all and take the plane to New York. I give that some serious thought, but then I know damn well if I get off the plane in New York, I'd be spotted within two minutes. I'd be in their home base too, and that's no good. I can't go that way. I got to get my balls together and walk right outside. So I grab my suitcase and I walk casual, right out the door you take when you're arriving in Washington and you need a cab. And everybody again looks as though they're waiting to eat me alive. Cops are there with guns on them, the kind of cops I got to be afraid of. No question in my mind that the police are on the take; whether they got this particular crew that I'm walking out into or not is immaterial. A cop could turn around and say, 'Wait, thief! Wait!' and shoot me and say, 'Gee, I just seen that guy steal that suitcase he's got in his hand there and he was running away and I told him to stop and he didn't.' And he'd be a big hero with the mob and the police department and everything else. And poor old Johnny Forza's stiff as a board on the ground.

Anyway, I got to get into a taxicab and get downtown to the bus station. A bus, there's another sweat. Any avenue of transportation is a sweat, but I can't go out walking or thumbing a ride, that's for sure. Instead of going to the bus station direct, I get in this guy's cab and tell him, 'Listen, I don't want to go in that bus station because I don't like crowds.' I'm telling him, 'Is there some place I can stop on the highway and catch a Baltimore

95

bus?' And the driver says there is, and he'll take me right there. So, he tears out of the airport and turns away from Washington and goes down the highway and I'm saying to myself, 'Look at this bum, he's building up a taxi fare on me, and then again he might be looking to take me in some bad place.' I got to be suspicious of everybody and everything because there's nobody that's above it. I mean I got one or two marshals that I think I can trust and that's about it in the whole goddamn country. There's nobody else but Nancy that I can trust. Nobody.

After a few miles I tell the driver to turn around and go to the bus station, that I changed my mind about the highway, and I know that this will make him remember me very well if anybody should happen to come around later asking questions. So we get to the bus station and I get off across the street. I know I want to end up in Philadelphia, but I don't want to leave any tracks to Philadelphia, so I go up to the ticket counter and tell the fella, 'I want a ticket to Baltimore please. When is the next bus?' And he tells me what time it leaves and how much it costs and I light a cigarette while he's making out the ticket. I pay for it, pick it up, and walk away.

'Hey, come back here a minute!' It's the guy behind the ticket counter. Right off the bat, I got jelly running down my back.

'What do you want?' I call to him from a dozen feet away. I'm getting ready to run out of there.

'Come over here for a minute, will you?' The guy's yelling at me again because I'm walking away.

'What do you want from me?' I'm saying back because, you know, I don't want to attract attention and this guy's still yelling for me, the damn fool. 'Come back here,' and he holds up my cigarette lighter. 'You forgot your lighter.' A sigh of relief comes over me and I think to myself that I can't do this no more. I got to get someplace safe and get there fast. So I walk back and apologize for yelling at the guy and I take my lighter and I take off. You see, my mind isn't working the way it's supposed to. Fear has got the best of me, and any change of pattern that I don't expect makes me nervous. I can recall any number of times when I was in real danger and I had no trouble with nerves. Like waiting outside a guy's place with a shotgun under my coat and acting casual when a cop car slowed down and gave me the once-over. But then I had friends backing me up and now I got no one.

I got about fifteen, twenty minutes here until the bus loads up and, as usual, it goes very slow. The driver and his buddies stand around with their paper cups of coffee shooting the breeze and they don't give a damn if your feet are killing you or you're a lady holding a kid or whatever. Until the driver's ready, you just stand. Finally, they call the damn thing and I slouch along hoping no one's looking my way and I get on and find a seat by myself about three rows back of the driver. I want to be near the door. And we take off for Baltimore.

I sit back and take a deep breath and light a cigarette. I'm shaking a little. And, you know, I don't need this. I'm tired of every time somebody looks at me I'm ready to whack them. I got to get someplace where I can get a night's sleep and not worry. A place where I can lie low for a while, a cabin in the woods, a farm. Somewhere I'll be safe. Now, I know this is nutty cause there's nowhere I'm going to be safe until I whack Butch out or drop off the end of the world. I'm looking out the window here and I see nothing but passing lights and I'm wishing I could lie down somewhere, and you know what I'm thinking of? I'm thinking about a church, and that's funny since I ain't been in one for years except for a funeral or some other family thing. But anyway I'm thinking if there was only a big church around here or a convent or whatever, I could check in there for a while and be safe. Even the mob lets you have sanctuary in the House of God. They nail you right outside the door, but while you're in there, no one's going to lay a glove on you. And I'm thinking on this and the more I think about it the better it sounds. Now, there was a guy out of Buffalo, I think, that did this a couple of years ago. He and some other guys had knocked off some made men. Maybe they knew it, maybe they didn't. Anyway, the guys who did this were all hit, but this one guy was allowed to live. And then he did the wrong thing – he got mad and threatened to kill one of the bosses, and this is a thing you don't even joke about and live. So he knew he was a dead man and he took off and wound up in one of them places out west where the monks live on a farm and raise grapes and make wine. And he was there working out in the fields for months and no one did a thing. Peaceful, nothing but crickets at night. But being in a monastery is a little like being in the joint. I mean, they ring a bell early in the morning, you got to get up and go out and work, and the food is good but there's nothing else to do. There's no women, no liquor, and sometimes no meat, and them guys don't talk much either. I mean it's not much of a life. Anyway, that's the reason I figure this guy did what he did, which was to leave and go into Los Angeles or somewhere and call up one of his former friends, and weeks later they found what was left of him. Like any wiseguy, he couldn't stay away from where the action was.

I think that's the way it happened, but all priests are not standup guys. What I mean is not that I'd worry about a priest whacking me out, but if he was the wrong kind he just might pass the word on where I was, and then they'd be waiting for me when I checked out of the church or wherever. You may not believe it, but some of them were even members back in Sicily. I swear it's true. There was one called Father Carmelo, an old Capuchin friar, and he was going around putting the arm on farmers with money.

He'd tell them that he had information that they were going to get whacked if they didn't give him money to pay off the bandits. You know what? They found later that this old priest and three others had this shakedown going with some *mafiosi* from the next town. And all the fathers wound up in the can, believe it or not. Which is a long way of saying I can't trust nobody now.

There must be seven or eight empty seats on the bus, and all of a sudden this young, good-looking tomato comes and sits beside me and I say to myself, 'Why is she doing this? Could she be part of a setup?' But maybe she's just a hooker or someone friendly who wants to talk. Anyway, she starts a conversation with me, which makes me very unhappy. Now, normally, I would be pleased to have a young tomato come up and sit beside me. But this time I'm very suspicious, and when she asks for a match, I take out my cigarette lighter and when I'm palming the lighter in my hand I notice the initials 'JF' are on this gold Dunhill. I hope she don't spot this : girls have sharp eyes for small things like that. Does this tomato know who I am? Is she setting me up? Is she supposed to win my confidence, maybe take me to her room like a couple of guys that I happen to know from the old days that took a couple tomatoes to their room and when they were in the room certain people walked up and knocked. It was a setup. This is what I got in the back of my mind.

So that hour-long ride from Washington to Baltimore is just like torture to me. I'm saying to myself, 'Any minute now she's going to stick a knife in me, and in the dark no one will ever notice the difference.' I've got a reading light if I want, but everybody's in darkness and I don't want to turn it on. So it's cheap conversation back and forth and finally she says : 'You staying in Baltimore?'

'Well, yeah, I think I'm staying there.'

'Do you live there?'

'No, I live in Chicago. I'm just traveling through.'

'Well, what are you going to be doing in Baltimore?'

'Ah, just a little pleasure trip.'

Her eyes light up. 'Well, honey, I got an apartment in Baltimore. Why don't you come up and see me, and we'll have a little fun?'

I'm a pretty hep guy and always have been, but I say, 'Listen, are you in business for yourself?'

'What do you mean?' she says.

'You know what I mean,' I says, 'are you a hooker? It's as simple as that.'

'Well,' she says, 'I don't like to be called that, but I'm available for fun and parties, you know.' So, now I want to go along with the gag because I don't want to have her throw any suspicion on me. She's a good-looking broad. I say, 'Look, why don't you give me your phone number and your address? I got a couple of little business deals to complete tonight, but tomorrow morning I'll give you a phone call, or tomorrow night.' All the broad is thinking about is the money she's going to make off me, right? So, she starts to mark it down on a piece of paper and then goes into her purse and hands me a business card. She laughs a little and, 'What's your name?'

'Joe Carbo,' I tell her. I'm thinking I haven't used that one for years. You know, guys on the lam usually use their own first name or one that sounds like it, so's you turn around when someone says it. Makes them easier to find. But, I always use a different name, like Frank Carpi, and I tell people I like them to use my middle name, Ron, which sounds like John when you yell it.

'Where are you staying?'

'Well, I don't really know,' I'm pretending to think about it. 'I gotta visit some friends first and then I don't know where I'll be staying, but don't worry, I'm going to get in touch with you.' So we have another cigarette together and talk some more, and then we're getting into the bus terminal and she says, 'Can I buy you a drink?'

She's smiling, but I can almost feel the knife in my ribs. I think it's about time she and I separated. And I say to her, 'Yeah, okay, but I'll tell you what to do. The bar's right across from the terminal? Okay, look, I want to confirm some tickets to Chicago for next week. I'll see you over there in ten minutes.'

'You're sure?'

'Yeah, don't worry about it. I'm going to be there. Here's five dollars for the first drink.' And I give her five and off she goes. And I take off out the other door and back to the ticket agent again and I buy a ticket now for Philadelphia on the nearest bus, the first thing moving. The guy tells me there's one in twenty-seven minutes.

Before I go looking for the bus, I remember some people in Baltimore that could help me – a couple of black guys I once had on my payroll in New York that I helped out. I saved them from getting arrested a few times by going to the bagman for the law. Now that they're in Baltimore I hear they spread out and are heavy with narcotics here, making a lot of money. Maybe I could trust one of them. I don't remember their whole phone number, but I remember the last four figures which is all you need. I go to a phone booth and the operator gives me the number when I tell her the place is on the east side of town. So, one of the guys answers the phone.

'Barney, you know who this is?'

'Uh, no. Who is it?'

'You can't recognize me?' I'm a little pissed off. 'I don't want to talk over your phone.'

'Oh, yeah. I know who it is. Hi, how are ya? What's going on?'

'I need some help, Barney. I need it bad.'

'Sure,' he says real friendly, 'come on over.' And oh-oh, it hits me like a shot. 'I'm going to give you my address,' he says. And I'm thinking, this guy's too willing. He knows what's going on, you know what I mean? He knows if he gives any protection to me he can get hurt, but he's so willing. Maybe he don't mean no harm, but can I take the chance? I say, 'Okay,' cause now I'm chilled right up the back. If he had said to me, 'Gee, John, you know I'd like to help but I'm kind of leery ...' and I had to beg a little bit and he says, 'Well, all right, we were friends before, don't come to my house, meet me at such and such a street corner, okay? I can just give you some money, that's all I can do.' If he'd said that instead of, 'Yeah, come on over,' I'd have felt a lot better. For him to invite me to his house, I know that he's got it in his mind, just as soon as he hangs up, to get on that phone to New York and say, 'I got him here, what do you want me to do with him?' See? So, I'm going along with it and I say, 'Gee, I'm glad you're doing this for me ...' and all the time, I'm thinking, 'Fuck you, you bastard. You think I was born yesterday.' And I'm getting mad at myself for being so stupid to even consider trusting him. I know the guy's earning through the mob and why should he jeopardize it for me? So I go through the motions of taking Barney's address down and I hang up and walk out and crumple the paper up and throw it in a wastebasket as I head for the Philadelphia bus.

I'm going to Philadelphia because, like I said, I got some friends there and I might be able to do something with them. And I'm going because I got no place else to go. I want to get out of Baltimore, especially now that I told this guy I was here. A bum wrong move on my part because by telling him, he knows when I don't show up that I took it on the lam again. So Butch will know where I was at this particular time and it's just a question of him taking a shot that I don't have a car and checking out all public transportation. I should have never made that phone call. I told you my mind isn't working right. But it's not that I did it because I'm dumb, it's that I'm half-crazy with not being around anyone I know or can trust.

And it's like I don't even care if I can trust them as long as I know them. I called Barney because I wanted to talk to some guy that I know – any guy, no matter what side he's on. And for a minute I had a friend on the line and then he turned out not to be a friend, but at least he was an enemy I knew.

I know exactly what Butch is going to do right now. He's going to send some people into Baltimore to canvass this whole area, and he's going to start at the bus and train stations because he knows I got very little money. He's going to find people who work in these terminals and they're going to spot my picture around and sooner or later someone's going to say, 'Hey, yeah, he bought a ticket from me to go to Philadelphia.' And then he'll move his troops to Philadelphia and do the same thing all over again. He's got the patience for it. The only hope I got is that I can move fast enough to keep ahead of him. So, I'm just gonna take my shot and get to Philadelphia and see what happens when I get there.

And I'm thinking that maybe there were two or three guys at the airport and maybe one of 'em was close and saw me jump off the walkway. And he might not have followed me down if he didn't have a piece on him. Maybe he just went back and called Butch, which would have saved him the trouble of laying people out there in these other airports. You know, all the time it's going through my mind, these guys are going to try and put a snatch on me because that little creep Butch is going to want to do me in himself. He's going to want to hurt me. This way he'd be a hero with all his mob and the Old Man. He'd say, 'Don Mario, I got this man myself. I had my people pick him up. We spotted, we waited, we tapped phones, we done this and that.' And Butch has given strict instructions : 'I want Johnny Forza alive. If you gotta bang him on the head that's okay, but I don't want anyone to shoot him or knife him or anything. Make sure he's in chains.'

Now my bus is ready to go and I take a good look around and make sure that I don't see any familiar faces. But I don't see anybody and the bus rolls out of the station. This time no one's sitting next to me. I got my suitcase on that seat. And I'm thinking about how lousy it is not to be in a position to trust anybody. And how we used to set guys up. Always a good friend got the action, a guy who calls the fella up and says, 'Hey, let's go out tonight, I got a couple of girls out on the Island.' And they drive out and on the way the guy stops for gas and while the friend goes into the men's room, some guys come out of the station and blast the guy waiting in the car. There's a million ways and it's easy, except when the guy knows he's in trouble with the mob and might get hit. A guy like that – like me right now – is buried so deep that you got to coax him out with something he really needs, like money. He's not going to come out for dinner or a tomato.

There might be a situation where a friend of mine comes along and says, 'Listen, Johnny, I got a chance to move a trailer load of stolen cigarettes tonight and I can't get no help. If you help me, I'll give you a percentage of it.' Or he says, 'We got a house we can invade tonight. I need someone to go with me. There's about a hundred grand stashed someplace.' And I need money very bad and I say to myself, 'Jesus, I know I can't trust nobody, but maybe I got to trust somebody to go and get the money.' And this would drag me out of my hole a little bit – maybe just enough to get whacked out. I know money can be my downfall.

It wasn't always that way. My mother and father were very poor, naturally, coming from East Harlem. No one was rich there. You know, a lot of people think that all of Harlem went black years ago, but that's not true. There's some blacks and a lot of Puerto Ricans in East Harlem, but there's streets like the one I grew up on – 116th between First and Second Avenues – that's still solid Sicilians and Italians.

My old man wasn't a knockaround guy; he was just a hardworking sucker. He done his best to support my mother and me and my brother and two sisters and we were very close. We all helped out, especially at a holiday. Like most Italians we couldn't let anything stand in the way of our enjoying that holiday. We might go without shoes the better part of the rest of the year or walk around in shabby clothes, but when it came to a holiday it was like a religion that we had to have new suits and dresses and shoes. It was the same thing with Butch and the rest of us.

I remember when I was a kid we used to have what they called Post Santa and you wrote just your name on a postcard, and sure enough the truck would come down before Christmastime. All the kids in the neighborhood got a present, something cheap like a fifteen-cent toy. One year Butch and I set up a big Post Santa robbery. The two guys who stood on the back of the truck and handed out presents were rummies, so when they were busy we went around and slashed the two front tires. And when I say truck, I mean they came around in a big Mack dump truck with all the things wrapped pretty – little dolls, stockings, handkerchiefs, lead soldiers, and things like that. Anyway, when they went to move the truck they felt the tires go down and they got out to look and they were cursing, 'You rotten little Guinea bastards. When I get you I'll break your mother's twat. You little wops, we're trying to help you and this is what you do to us.' And while they were doing all that yelling, Butch and I was in the back there filling up two or three burlap sacks full of toys and running like hell with them. We sold them for about ten dollars. That ten bucks in them days to a poor family was a lot of money.

Now I did this with Butch one year but I never did it

105

again. He came around the next year telling me what day the Post Santa truck would be through, and I told him I had to be somewheres else. I tried to make like I was really sorry not to be in on it, but you know, after the first time I saw some of the little kids in the neighborhood and they were crying and carrying on and all like that about the truck never getting to their street and I felt like I'd really done a wrong thing. It was fun while we were doing it, but later I felt bad and wished we'd robbed somebody like Squieri the butcher, who could afford to lose a few. And we did just that a month later. I still feel that way about stealing. I'm not a Robin Hood, but I never did like to take advantage of a guy who couldn't afford it. Sometimes it worked out that way and I'd think, 'With all the good suckers around here, why did I have to nail this poor jerk?' It's like robbing the poorbox, nothing to be proud of.

Now, Butch didn't feel that way. He had a mean streak in him and he thought it was being tough. He'd do things for no reason, just to hurt somebody. Well, I guess he always had a reason but it wasn't easy to figure sometimes. Like the time they threw him out of St Anthony's School. He'd played hooky and got into fights like all of us did. And his grades were rotten. But the thing that finally did it was his mean streak. There was this kid in Butch's class name of Vincent Columbo, and he was athletic and very handsome and the girls all mooned around. Butch hated him and called him a fag behind his back. Anyway, one afternoon, just after Vincent had been voted most popular boy in his class, the bell rang and we all ran out into the hall to go home and we're shoving and yelling, and all of a sudden there's a girl screaming and we turn around and Vincent is standing over there in front of his locker and his face is white as a sheet and his shirt is covered with blood. Somebody had taped a couple of double-edge razor blades to the handle of his locker and when he pulled the door he slashed his hand so bad it looked like a hamburger. Then a kid remembered seeing Butch hanging around out there earlier and they found a half empty package of blades in his locker and he was kicked out. Now, that didn't stop me from being his friend, but it made me think about what Butch might do if he hated somebody. I think a lot about it now.

# CHAPTER FOUR

It's early morning in Philadelphia, still pitch dark out, and I need a place to sleep. As usual, the bus station is on skid row but instead of going to a flophouse that can be checked and where someone might remember me, I walk down the street and slip into an all-night movie. There aren't too many customers and I sit down right in the middle, with my suitcase on my knees. And I watch the movie for a while, something about soldiers in a war or whatever, and pretty soon I'm nodding and then I wake up when the guns start shooting. I look at my watch and it's almost seven in the morning and I feel like I had been through a war.

I get up and go to the men's room of the moviehouse. It's real crummy, with piss on the floor and a guy sitting on a toilet passed out. But the water runs and I splash some on my face and wash the talcum out of my hair and comb it straight back the regular way. I also dump those airline coveralls in the garbage can there, push them down under the paper towels and all the other crap. And I change my clothes. My suit goes into the case and I switch to blue jeans and a blue shirt, knockaround clothes I always carry to wear sitting around motels and places. It's partly a disguise, but also I might wind up doing some work for money to get out of town. I step out into the sunlight and stop in the first diner I come to for coffee and doughnuts.

And I'm thinking, I'd like to believe my friends in this town are real friends, but I know they're not. They were friends of mine not because they liked me but because of who I used to be. And I need money now, and that makes me realize I got to be very careful. I need to have some time to think about getting back to New York and getting my stash – just over $600,000 in a box in the Irving Trust down on Broadway and Wall. And I want to get ahold of my sweetheart and take the hell off out of here. I'm wondering how tight Butch has got the bank covered when I suddenly think, why not raise an army, a five- or six-man army, and go in and whack out Butch and maybe even take over from the Old Man?

It may sound like them war movies got into my head, but recruiting an army of guys is the simplest thing in the world. It's been done. You start hanging around rough neighborhoods and, all of a sudden, some guy recognizes you and he becomes a hero worshipper. He figures, 'Hey, this guy made a million dollars, and let me hang around with him, I'm not going to say nothing to nobody, maybe it'll rub off on me.' So now you brainwash the guy a little bit, and say, 'Well, geez, if I could get half-a-dozen guys together and go back to New York, there's a ton of money there waiting for us.' It's not hard to visualize talking some dimwitted fools with a lot of guts into doing this. I might even get some guys out from under Butch himself. You know, as Butch is sending his troops all over the place looking for me, he's got to wonder if they're all loyal to him. He's got to figure that some of them were close to me and maybe they still got some sympathy, no matter what I done. Maybe they even know why I done it. So Butch has got to worry about his back all the time. We all had to worry about that all the time. Only now, with him, it's a little more.

So I sit there with my coffee and the sunlight coming in the window and I feel pretty good, but the more I think about raising an army the more I think it's not too feasible an idea. I mean it can be done, but I can't tell these five or six men I pick up, 'I want to go there strictly for revenge.' They would want to go there for practical reasons – for cash, for power, for running up the ladder a little higher. But just to go there to whack Butch and no profits? They're not going to do it. And if I don't tell them revenge is what I want and they find out later, they're going to turn around and whack me out. So I smile to myself at the dream. I've got to use my head here. If I can get a pop at Butch, fine. If I can't, I better put these thoughts of revenge out of my mind and think about just escaping. What I need now is walking-around money, enough to get me to New York and keep me until I can get a clear shot at the bank. While I'm eating there some guys in work clothes come and go and I think about going down to the docks for a day's work. It's not far from where I am now, and I remember they pay you by the day in cash. There's a big risk that I'm going to bump into people there who are connected, but the good thing is they won't ask for identification. In other words, I walk in and they say, 'You're hired. Okay, what's your name?' And I say, 'John Jones.' They couldn't care less.

I know the docks well. Years ago I spent some time working on the Brooklyn piers. Not really working, but checking up to see who the troublemakers were that were giving the union a hard time. The boss says, 'Look, I want to find out who's starting all this commotion.' So I walked up to the gang boss and he'd say, 'Forza, you work in hold number thirteen.' And I knocked around there for a while and actually done some work and I find out who the union breakers are, and me and a couple of other people, Butch too, work the same deal and we find out that this black guy and this Irish guy are trying to go against mob rule there. They want to take over themselves. So one day we catch them down below on the job and we give the Irishman a serious beating with a two-by-four and we don't hurt the yam. We tell him this is just an example of what'll happen if he don't get in line with the rest of the outfit there.

So I go back to the station and check my bag, and then I'm walking towards the Philadelphia docks and wondering if I'll see any faces I know. There's danger going there but I got to take the shot because I got only twenty-nine dollars and change now. I still got that government check, but it's got the Carpi name on it and I don't want to try cashing it. The marshals may be on to me and have the word out that I'm lamming. I come to this big gate and I can smell the water and there's a bunch of fellas around like I presume there is every morning. And then I see a fat slob of a gang boss and he's looking over some papers. He's one of these pricks who laughs a lot but don't smile. He stands up on a wooden box and, 'Okay, I need eleven extra men this morning.' And everybody puts up their hand that wants to work, and the gang boss laughs, 'Nice clean work, a boat full of copper slabs, raw wool, and hides.' This makes some of the guys pull their hands down. It sounds like dirty work. And I put up my hand there and he says, 'Okay, I want you, you, you, you.' And he picks me amongst other people and he says, 'Okay, report down to Dock C-Five, and the foreman down there'll tell you what to do.'

Anyway, I start moving and I look around at these brutes and I say to myself, 'If I get spotted here, I'll never leave this dock alive.' I'm a little scared now, but what am I going to do? I'll just go down with these guys and keep my eyes open. I walk the whole length of the pier and I see Dock C-Five way down at the end, maybe a quarter of a mile away. The thing is, I'm sorta trapped out here. I'm getting to the end of this long pier with ships tied up on my left and on the right-hand side there's one long, big warehouse. No easy way out of here except back to the front gate, and to get there you got to pass the clock-house where the gang boss sits and where you punch in and punch out. If trouble comes, that guy is going to know about it and the gate will be shut to me. So, I got to figure another way out of here and I'm looking things over, and across the river from where I am I see that within a matter of maybe three hundred yards there's a spot where I could get up on land if I had to jump into the water. So I look around for a rowboat and a way to get out of the water on the other side of the river because I got to plan my escape now.

I finally come to C-Five and it's a big, black boat with a stack and cabins painted white and green. The boat fore-man is standing by the gangway there and I give him my name. He says, 'Okay, I want you working down in num-ber-one hold, loading pallets and nets. Get yourself a hook and gloves.' You see, if you need that stuff, they supply it. So I get to the hatch and it's a long way to the bottom – maybe fifty, sixty feet. And you have to climb down an iron ladder they have welded right to the side. So I go over the side and start to climb down and I don't like to do it, never did like it. Too easy to fall off these ladders. They're all greasy and sometimes the rungs are loose and you take a step and the thing falls off and you're hanging there.

I seen a guy once that had a sack over his shoulder with stuff he'd picked up, a couple of bottles of whiskey or something, and he's climbing the ladder one-handed and holding onto the sack with the other hand. And he's climbing up, up, up and near the top, he grabs a rung that gives way. He don't let go of his bag, he just holds onto the rung and it comes away in his hand and he's still holding it and he falls, wham, down to the bottom of the hold. And I'm thinking about that guy as I climb slowly down, looking straight ahead so I won't get dizzy. Any-way, I get there and I'm sweating a bit and thinking how it won't be easy to get out in a hurry. I'm standing on something soft and the whole place is full of bales of some kind of animal hides all wrapped up in dirty gunny sacks and the place stinks and it's full of dust and dirt.

There's a big black guy, the real black kind we used to call a *mulinyam*, an eggplant, when I was a kid. And he's working by himself pulling bales down with his hook and horsing them out to the net and making a pile and yelling, 'Take it away.' They put me in the dirtiest hold of all, the bastards. But what the hell, it's still real money, maybe a hundred for a day's work down here. And I don't have to fear the yam, he's just a poor slob trying to earn a living. Of course, poor slob or not, if someone says, 'Hey, get that guy!' he'll come after me and that's what I got to be careful of.

I finally go to work and it's hot and dirty but not all that bad, better than sitting in a motel room with a bunch of marshals. Swinging the hook is almost fun. I can hit the bale as hard as I want and jerk it out and hit again. And I'm thinking as I hit and pull that this is Butch that I'm working over and I hit harder and harder, trying to sink this hook deep in him. I'm hitting and pulling and working up a sweat and I see the yam out of the corner of my eye standing there doing nothing and looking at me. I stop and turn and, 'What are you looking at?'

'Nothing, man,' he gives me the big smile. 'I just thought you flipping out, you 'tacking that bale like it's a wild beast.' And he's right. That's just what it is I'm doing, attacking Butch with this hook and if I don't rip him apart with it he's going to get me. And I laugh and joke with the yam, who's not a bad guy after all. I tell him I was using the hook thinking about a guy got eyes for my girlfriend. This yam is older than the ones you see on the street carrying radios and slapping hands. He's a hard worker and he looks like he been down here a hundred years. He knows just how to hook a bale to move it with the least work. Not lazy, just good at the job. And you know, it's not so crummy down here. I'm in good shape. My arms are going to hurt tomorrow, but I can do the work easy. I could deck Butch right now if I had to. I always was a little better than him with my hands, even if he's got longer arms.

And, I'm thinking, Butch is not the same kind of guy he was when we was standing together. Over the years, he got so he was all the time plotting and planning, acting more like a don than anything. Always a frown on his face like he's thinking big things and he nods his head when you talk to him as much as to say, 'Yes, I know all that — and more.' He turned out to be a user, got guys working for him in the mob and broads that are everywhere — hospitals, City Hall, Motor Vehicle, banks. That's what makes him so valuable. Whether the Old Man likes him or not, he's got to admit that Butch is a valuable man. Like I said, he's got a superior memory and he marks everything he's told about anybody. The Old Man, Scordato, don't know it, but he's got stuff on him, too, like who the Old Man goes to see in his spare time, because he's got his own *goumara,* you see? Anyway, my point is, you can't lead and stay behind a desk, you got to go with them on the tough jobs sometimes. It's good to have smarts like Butch, but not good enough. You have a boss that's never broke an egg, no matter how much smarts he's got you can't have the same respect for him as you got for a guy who wasn't too high and mighty to whack someone out when it had to be done.

Me and the yam take a short break. It's hot and dusty and I fill my mouth with water and swish it around and spit it out and then take a real drink. We got a metal jug down with a spout on the side and you hold it up and let the water run into your mouth. It even feels good running down my chin. I sit down for a minute, take off my gloves, and see I'm getting a couple blisters on my hand right through the glove. I remember my old man coming home with his hands so tough he'd put out matches with his fingers. He was a stonemason, and his clothes would be white with dust. He's dog-tired and he takes a bath and sits down with a glass of wine and tells me it feels good to do a day's work. And I respected my old man, don't get the wrong idea, I really did. It's just that I had a taste for the high life that wiseguys seemed to live. You know, sleep late, dress well, sit around a club all night and have people come over and kiss your ass. My old man went to work at five in the morning with a paper bag full of onions and bread, and even the wiseguys respected him and we never wanted for food on the table. But I wanted more. I saw the power the mob had. If you met one of them and you weren't one of them, you treated him with plenty of respect, because otherwise he could hurt you and your family here. He could send one letter back to the Old Country and your whole family back there in Sicily'd be wiped out. I remember when I was a kid, I don't really remember, but I heard about it plenty. There was this cousin of my old man, name of Sal Intiso, who was on the fringes of the mob and was getting out of line. He did crazy things on his own, like moving into another guy's territory. So he was warned and warned, and he made the mistake of threatening one of the dons. Anyway, they told Sal that if he didn't get in line something bad would happen to his brother in the Old Country. And Sal told the guy who warns him to go back and tell the don to go shit in his hat and if anything happens to his brother he's going to come over and blow his brains out. Well, within two weeks, Sal's brother, his wife, and three kids got wiped out by shotgun blasts on their farm in Sicily. The local papers blamed it on bandits, but nothing was stolen. Sal got the message, but it wasn't really meant for him. He was whacked out the following month. The message was for everybody else.

Anyway, my old man never liked that I went with the wiseguys, but he always took my side. He wasn't just a father, he was a friend, and it makes a big, big difference when you can introduce your father to a friend of yours and say, 'This is my father, and he's my pal too.' We went to ball games together, we played *boccie* together, and when I was in trouble I could go to him. I remember the first time I said, 'Pa, I done this thing wrong, I stole this money and they're gonna arrest me.' And, no matter if he hated my guts for what I done, he was with me, you understand? He put his back right up against the wall with me and he fought the whole world for me. That's the way Italian fathers are. That's why Butch was so hurt when he used to see his mother beat up, and he'd jump on his father's back and try to stop him, and he'd get the worst of it, naturally – he was only a kid. And I'm feeling sorry for him for a minute and I got to stop that. So he had a creep for an old man. So what?

And it comes to lunchtime now, and the yam quits working and sits down and opens up a bag of sandwiches. And suddenly I'm very hungry. So he tells me there's a hotdog wagon that comes around up on the pier and I make it up the ladder fast looking for something to eat. Sure enough, down there maybe fifty feet from the boat is a hotdog wagon under a big red umbrella, and guys are standing around eating. So I go down the gangway and over and get a pair with chili and a coffee. And I'm sitting down on a crate to eat and I look up and there's the gang boss coming down the pier. He goes to the hotdog wagon and gets a coffee and he nods over at me and stands there blowing on his coffee. I pay no attention to him and eat my food. A couple minutes later, I get up, light a cigarette, and stroll back to the gangway. I turn to look back and the boss is still standing there jawing with the hotdog man. And I turn to the foreman and ask him if he's got anything else I can do. I tell him the hides stink and he grins and says, 'Down below in the hole, same one you was working before.' And I'm thinking the son-of-a-bitch called it 'hole' not 'hold' because he knows it's like the hole in the can with no windows, where they throw you in for breaking the rules.

So I'm on deck now and I'm starting to feel a little funny about the gang boss. Why did he walk all the way down here to have a cup of coffee? Would he leave the clockhouse at all without his being sent? Did someone make me and send him down to see if I was where I was supposed to be? Or am I being nervous? I mean, maybe the slob makes the rounds once a day. He could use the exercise. I don't know, but I'm getting a little tingle on the back of my neck and I think I better pay heed to that. I'm starting to feel now that this being on the run is bad business, that I'm going to catch it soon, quicker than I thought. There's just too many of these people around looking. The odds are no good. A sucker bet. And I figure that maybe the best thing I can do now is get in touch with Mister Oakes. Maybe he can bring me back in or something.

Now, this boat is tied up to a dock and so it has a phone on it, a pay phone that they hook up right on the deck. So, I go over to the phone, and the foreman down on that dock can't see me anymore, and I try and reach Mister Oakes at his office in Washington. He's out and I get a Mister Jones on the line. I remember him, he's one of the marshals that goes by the book, but I can't be choosy. I feel I'm in serious trouble and I got no way out, so I tell him I think I'm in danger. He says, 'Well, it's too bad, but you're going to have to get out of it on your own, son. We're not taking care of you.'

And I'm saying, 'Where's Mister Oakes?'

'Well, Mister Oakes can't have anything to do with you anymore.'

'Who said so? I'd like to hear that from him.'

'I say so because I'm Mister Oakes's boss.' And the son-of-a-bitch don't give a damn about me. In fact, he drops a little hint, 'Where are you, Forza? Don't you understand you're in violation of your parole? You're supposed to be in Arizona.'

'How am I going to protect myself from these people?' I ask him. I don't have time to argue about the parole regulations. But he's a book man, 'Remember,' he says, 'you're on parole. You break any law at all – assault, getting yourself a gun, doing things under an illegal name or anything – you're going back to prison, Mister Bigshot, and that's all there is to it.'

Now I know that's the end of it, and Jones will not give me any help at all. 'Who can I call?' I ask him.

'Call anyone you want,' he says, 'Call your local police.' This guy is a real comic – he knows as well as I do that local cops are usually up tight with the mob. I call the police and I'm a dead man. So I know I'm lost. I hang up the phone.

I got a couple of choices now. I can make a run for it back to the main gate and they might catch me at the clockhouse or before. I can try to get down to a rowboat and they'll probably see me do it. Or, I play Mickey the Dunce and go do what the foreman told me. Mickey's a stupid guy, right? I make out like I don't see nothing wrong and go back down there.

So I'm in the hole again working away and my senses are all on edge because I know that coming back down here was a dumb thing to do, but I also know that this is the best place to hide. I can try going through a watertight door into another hold, or maybe I can find the hatch to the shaft alley and get into the engine room and hide and get away later. I know these clowns won't know how to search a boat and they won't want to nose it around anyway. So I'm waiting for the yam to take a leak so's he won't know where I went, and I'm thinking maybe I'm making a mistake. They might not of made me at all. I been working here more than an hour when all of a sudden, I hear someone coming down that long ladder.

It's iron and you can hear anything that touches it. And I look and the yam is standing near the cargo net and he is almost turning white so I know that there's something wrong. I'm farther back in the shadows and I'm looking, and finally I see legs in coveralls coming down the ladder and as the guy comes down, right on top of him is another set of legs. The only trouble is that both these guys are wearing shiny black shoes.

Even the yam looks up and says, 'Uh, oh. This looks like trouble, man, for somebody.' He says, 'You in trouble?'

'Not me. I want no part of this,' I guess I say. This old-timer has seen some bad goings-on around here, like strikebreakers and guys getting their heads busted. Anyway, I grab my hook and I don't run, I walk behind some bales and I see the first guy get off the ladder, and start wandering around like he's lost. This guy's not a worker, he never been down in a boat before. And he sees the yam standing there and says, 'Hey, you! Get out of here.' And the black man doesn't say a word. He just runs up that goddamn ladder as fast as he can go.

And that leaves me alone with two guys I know are looking for me. One of them I sort of recognize. I mean, I think I recognize him, but I think I recognize a lot of guys now. They both got guns, and one guy whispers to the other and points over in my direction. In the meantime, I'm playing it nice and quiet. My breath sounds to me like it's thunder ever time I breathe. The sweat's running down me and I'm feeling a little wobbly and thinking this might be it. I'm not trying to be a hero, but I'll pull the son-of-a-bitches' eyes out with this hook before I go down. I been in plenty of street fights and there was none of this hand-to-hand movie baloney. When you fight you bite, kick, gouge, and use a ballbat, shank, or whatever. So, one guy's heading right towards me and I say to myself, 'Well, now we'll see.' Just as he gets around the bale I've been hiding behind, he glances the other way, and when he does I swing the hook and catch him right in the throat and yank back hard and he's down at my feet. A couple of good kicks in the head and he's out of it.

I shake the guy down and take a gun and a knife off him. Now this other guy must have heard something because when I stand up from searching the first guy, I see something move and – bang – he pegs a shot at me. I drop to the dirt and start crawling out from behind that bale to the left, figuring he'll think I'll go right. And I crawl and crawl through that dirty, dusty crap for what seems like a mile and the guy's looking around and pointing the gun and starting to walk slowly to where I conked his partner. He gets part ways there and I take the knife I just got and throw it over the guy's head so it lands in the dirt behind him and makes a little noise. He turns quick and pegs a shot and when he turns I stand up and shoot him in the back and he goes down.

Now I know I got trouble because I had to shoot. The sound of the guns must have been heard all over the dock and they probably got other guys around. So, I jam the gun into my belt and start up the ladder as fast as I can move. I get up maybe twenty, thirty feet when I hear a shot below, and my right arm is on fire. I almost fall. The son-of-a-bitch is up and shooting at me. I should have finished him down there when I had the chance. I'm holding on with my left hand and looking down, and I see he's staggering to the ladder and trying to climb up after me and he's aiming another shot. Thank God he misses me. I'm bleeding like a stuck pig and trying to climb up using my left hand and hugging the ladder with my right. I can use the arm but it hurts like hell and I don't trust my right hand to hold on.

By the time I get up to the deck I can hardly pull myself over the edge of the hatch and when I do I fall down and hit my right shoulder and think I'm going to pass out from the pain. The guy down below is yelling, 'Stop! Stop him!' And while nobody can hear him, I see some guys running around on the pier and I know there's going to be cops here in a few minutes. I'm as much afraid of them as I am of Butch's people. They catch me and I either get shot escaping or they send me to the joint for parole violation. And if the guy I took the gun off of is dead, then it's murder one, but who the fuck cares? If they put me back in I'm dead anyway. And I'm standing there holding my shoulder with my left hand and wondering where to go when I hear somebody yelling over the side of the boat and the next thing I know a bunch of guys come up the gangway and onto the deck. It's the black guy and three, four others, and the yam is screeching his head off, 'I seen it all! I seen it all! They come down the ladder and, I didn't do nothing. I had nothing to do with it.' The guy's copping a plea and I got to get out of here. One stiff downstairs and one guy banged up who's just about there, and I'm bleeding all over the place and all I can see is me backed into a trap. I do the only thing I can, the thing I was thinking about before – go over the side and into the water.

It's a long ways down and I jump feet first without thinking about it. If I looked too long I wouldn't have jumped. The water is cold and I feel it ringing in my ears. I come back up and I'm between the pier and the boat with those big rope bumpers over my head that keep the ship from banging into the dock. I'm holding onto a log or a big piece of wood and it's greasy with dirt and there's all this shit down here and the water's oily and full of tar and floating garbage. I can hear people up on the dock, yelling and running around and somebody throws a rope down and they're going to slide down to the water and see if they can find me.

So, I let go of the timber and get back under the dock

as far as I can. It's a crisscross mess of wooden poles all slippery with seaweed or something. I try to hold on and pull myself up a little, but I can't get a hold, and my shoulder is starting to pain something awful. I'm waiting and I figure they won't see me, but if they got a flashlight then I'm gone. I lost the gun when I hit the water. I ain't prayed to God since I was a kid, but I'm mumbling a little prayer now that I get through this. I pray that He keeps me so that I can get to Butch and then to Nancy. The more I think of this the warmer I get, and pretty soon the water don't seem cold at all.

Now I realize that it's got very, very quiet up on the dock. They must be listening to see if they can hear me down here. The rope's not moving. Maybe they're doing something else. Maybe there's a way down here in back of me, and I'm trying to turn and see but it's dark. And then I hear a noise that I hate most of the times, but this time it's okay – a siren and the sound of a cop car driving right up on the dock. Butch's people must have taken off. Someone called the police and, for once, they got here in the nick of time, just like on television. The difference is that I can't let them see me either, so I got to get out of here before they go down that rope or come looking in a rowboat, because whoever called the cops probably said they heard shots and seen me go over. So I get out there between the boat and the dock and I find that log I was holding onto or another one, I can't tell, and I use it to help get through the water and down toward the back end of the boat. It's very slow going because there's so much junk in the water and I can hear the cops up above talking and yelling.

And I'm pushing along the side of the boat and pushing and moving away from them. After a long time, I get to the rudder, which is way out of the water now and I sure hope nobody starts the engines while I'm back here. I'd get sucked right into the propellor like a meat grinder. Now I can see the other side of the river and it looks like three-quarters of a mile away. To my right is a big bridge with cars coming over on it. I'm still holding onto this piece of wood because I don't think I could get over there without it. My shoulder hurts so I can only paddle with one arm.

I been riding on the log, keeping my head and shoulders out of the water, but now I got to hang onto it so only my head shows and hope they don't see me. I close my mouth tight and push away from the side with my legs, wondering if anybody on deck is going to look down. I got to be easy to spot right here in the middle of the river. Like I never believed them war movies where the guy is swimming about ten feet away from the Germans and splashing along and they never see him. No way they wouldn't see him unless he was swimming underwater. So now I'm maybe fifty feet from the boat and moving slow, too slow. I look up and I can't see anybody on the deck; they must be over on the other side looking for me. And then I see a guy's head and he's turning this way so I let go of the log and I'm underwater holding my breath and counting to myself. 'One, two, three, four . . .' And I got to get air so I come up and the guy is gone and I'm worrying if he saw me and went to get help.

Now I'm a hundred yards or so away from the boat and they can't see me even if they was looking. I begin to feel pretty good like I could stay here all day. The water was so cold I was freezing a while back but now it seems warm, and I don't even feel the pain in my arm much. The only thing that worries me, is my clothes are a mess. I know when I was a kid and played football in a cement park with no padding or nothing, Christ we all went home with ripped legs, but God forbid if you ripped your clothes. Your mother and father'd break your head. And here my clothes have oil and shit and stuff all over them. And Pa is going to be mad as hell when I get home . . .

I got my eyes closed and I'm sort of half dreaming all

this and I must have fallen asleep cause I suddenly got a mouth full of water. I'm choking and spitting and I feel cold and it's getting dark and here comes a motorboat downriver going like hell. It don't look like a police boat, but I can't take a chance even if it's not cops. I don't want anybody helping me out of the water and then taking me to the hospital. I pass out in the hospital, I wake up in the can. So I duck down under the log and my head's on the side away from the boat. It zooms past and a minute later the waves come and knock me around. And my arms hurt when I climb back on top of the log, but I'm laughing a little – laughing about the guy in hell who's treading water in a sea of shit and he thinks that's bad, but it's worse when the Devil comes by in a motorboat. It breaks me up.

I'm almost across the river now. There's no easy place to land here – no docks, no beach or nothing. It's built up six, eight feet off the water with rocks and timber all covered with green stuff. I push along a ways and pretty soon come to a sort of a gully where the wood and rock have fallen down. I push close and I feel rocks with my feet. I can stand up and I let go of the log and take a step and fall on my ass in the water. The rocks are smooth as glass. So I crawl out of the water and drag myself to the dry ground and it's a yard in back of an old factory full of rusty machines and junk. I lay there on the ground trying to get my breath and feeling good to be alive. I stretch out and close my eyes and I can feel myself falling asleep. It's not bad here, sort of like a hobo jungle.

I wake up after sleeping for only a minute or two. I started dreaming about being back in the can and suddenly it came to me that I'm out of my head to be laying around here like I had nothing to do but sleep. So I get to my feet, and my shoulder and arm are really hurting now and I'm getting stiff. I feel like my shoulder is swelled up and I must look like a hunchback. I'm beginning to worry about gangrene since the water I been in all day has got to have messed up the hole where the bullet went. I need a doctor and I can't go to the hospital. That means I need a mob doctor, the kind that don't give a damn what they do to make money, that will do what they're told and keep their mouth shut. On the whole East Coast there's maybe twenty-five, thirty doctors that are in the bag. In the city of Boston there's only three, and in New York there's seven or eight.

Like everything else, you memorize the names and numbers of mob doctors. It's all in the runaway sheet we have — a booklet that tells you where you can get help anywhere in the country, who to see for a place to stay in Chicago, who to see for a fake ID in Detroit. You memorize this thing and get rid of it. I know I got to be somewhere in Camden, New Jersey, which is across the river from Philadelphia and I remember there's a mob doctor in Trenton, which is not too far away. I'll go there and I'll think of the doc's name on the way. So, I walk through the factory yard, go around the building, and come to a wooden fence with so many boards gone that it's easy to step through into the street. I don't want to walk to the middle of town or take a bus because people are going to notice how bad I look. It's almost dark now and I'm going to wait until I can get a cab. I'm standing there and suddenly I realize that it was light when I passed out in that junkyard so it's got to have been hours ago. Finally, after about fifteen or twenty minutes, just as I'm about to try using a phone, an empty taxicab comes by and stops when I whistle. I tell the driver, 'Trenton, please, and I'll give you the address in a minute when I think of it.'

The taxi's tearing through the night to Trenton and I'm picturing in my mind the name of the doctor and it don't come, but I do get Hamilton Avenue and, I tell the guy, 'Look, I'm visiting a friend there in Trenton and he lives on Hamilton Avenue but I don't recall the number. Will ya stop at a phone and I'll call him?' So, he stops and I duck in the booth and call information and tell the girl it's an emergency and I want the address of my friend's doctor who lives on Hamilton Avenue. She tells me 401 North Hamilton for Doctor Jacobson. About ten minutes later, I pay off the driver in front of his house, a big brown shingle place, with a doctor sign on the lawn with a little light over it. Nice.

I knock on the door and ring the bell. Guy in a white coat comes and asks, 'Can I help you?'

'Uh, yeah. I fell down off a scaffold and hurt myself.'

The doctor says, 'Come on in,' and I follow him down a dark hall to an office in the back. Inside, he turns up the light and looks at me, and says, 'Hey, don't I know you?' You're Johnny Forza, right?'

'Yeah. Is there something wrong because I'm Johnny Forza? You help everybody else, you don't want to help me?' I never laid eyes on the guy before, but he knows my face, which means someone showed this jerk my picture. Meanwhile, the doctor's saying, 'Oh, no, no. No problem at all. Please sit right here so I can get a look at that.' And he cuts my shirt off and uses a bottle of alcohol and some cotton to clean my shoulder. I'm grinding my teeth it hurts so damn much.

'Johnny,' the Doctor says, 'lie down here and let me give you a shot to kill the . . .'

'No!' I yell. 'No, you're not giving me no needle to kill no pain. Take the slug outa me just the way it goes. I want to be awake to see you do it.'

'There's going to be an awful lot of pain, Mister Forza,' he says. And I know he's right and I'm sweating just thinking about it, but what can I do? I says, 'Sure, put me to sleep so you can make a phone call, huh? No sir, I'll pass that deal.'

So, he lays me down there on his operating table and I

say, 'I'm telling you ahead of time, you do anything wrong, I pick up one of these scalpels and cut your throat with it, understand.'

I hate going to fucking doctors, I've always hated the stink of their office and the shitty way they have of looking at you like you was a side of beef on a hook. In the joint they were always checking my rear end, lifting up my balls, looking at my feet, my hands, my fingernails. You know, it's kind of embarrassing to bend down and have a guy look up your asshole. It really is. But they don't give a damn; they always know they're in charge and you pretty much got to go along with them. One of the prison doctors was always doing the VD number : 'Pull it back, and milk it down and turn around and let's do it again next week.' I always figured the guy for a fairy.

Well, this one cleans the wound in my shoulder and begins looking for a bullet, sticking a little metal rod in there and I think I'm going through the roof with the pain. He says he's sorry and offers again to give me a shot. I pick up a scalpel and he goes back to work. And the phone rings. I jump. It's on the wall next to where I'm laying. It rings a couple of times and the doctor looks at me like, 'Do I answer?' I tell him to pick it up and hold it close so I can hear what's said. He reaches for the phone and I put the scalpel to his throat. 'This is Doctor Jacobson,' he answers, very professional, and holds the phone over to my ear.

'Listen, Doc,' says a heavy gravel voice, 'I'm a friend of the people in Brooklyn, see? And we understand an ex-friend of ours was hurt down near you. We want to know if he came to see you.'

'No, no. He hasn't been here,' says the doc, a little nervous.

'If you do see him or hear from him, here's a number to get in touch with us immediately. Write it down.' And the guys gives a New York phone number and I can't place the voice. 'If he comes to you, try and stall him and call us.'

'Yes. Yes, of course.' The doctor is starting to sweat.

'And Doc, if you do this we'll be very happy to return the favor. If you don't,' the guy's snarling a bit, 'we're not gonna like it.' He hangs up.

Jacobson goes back to work on me, but his hands are shaking. He grabs a pair of long-nose pliers and reaches in for the bullet and he's shaking and it hurts like hell. He stops, takes a couple of deep breaths and goes in again and out comes the bullet and he shakes some powder into the hole and bandages me up. I'm so weak from the pain I can hardly see straight and I'm saying to myself, 'Bastard! As soon as I walk out the door he's going to turn me in. There's no two ways about it. So there's only one thing I can do with this son-of-a-bitch.

'Well,' he says, 'sit up and we'll see how you feel.'

I say, 'Okay,' and I sit up carefully, trying not to use my right arm. I say, 'You know something, I think I hurt my leg too. While I'm sitting, why don't you take a look at it?' And, as he goes down there to take my shoe off and push up my pants, I reach over and grab a big glass ashtray and crown him as hard as I can with my left hand. He goes down and I jump down off the table. He's dizzy but not out and I'm so weak. He's stronger than I am but he don't know it, he's so scared. So, I smash him across the face and knock him out. But he's not going to be that way for long, so I rip some tape off a big roll he's got there and I tape his mouth and hands and ankles because as soon as this bird wakes up the hunt is going to get hot. They're going to know where I got fixed and how bad it is.

Now I hope there's no one else in the house, but even if there is the noise I just made was no more than I was making when he was digging the bullet out. So, I go through the guy's pockets and find about fifty bucks. In a drawer of his desk I find an envelope with about two hundred bucks and some checks. Now all I need is clothes. Mine are in my suitcase back in Philadelphia bus station, and there's no way I'm going back for them. I go upstairs very quietly with a scalpel in my hand and I don't see anybody. At the top there's a bedroom with closets full of clothes. I pull out a suit jacket, try it on, and it don't fit. The son-of-a-bitch is shorter and heavier than I am. I go out into the hall and there's some other closets. Nothing but blankets in one, old filing cabinets in the other. The room across from the bedroom turns out to be a den or something. There's a closet, too, and inside there I hit the jackpot: a lot of hunting and fishing stuff, jackets, coats, sweaters, boots, the works. It belongs to somebody else or the doc didn't used to be fat. Anyway, I pick my way through like I was in a store and find a pair of Army pants a little tight, but not bad. Then I take an old brown tweed jacket with leather patches and the sleeves are a little short, but it's okay with a black turtleneck under it. The boots and shoes are all either too big or too small or they're for fishing or snow or whatever. So I put on some lace-up boots a size too big and use two pair of socks.

'I'm back across the hall washing my face and I use the doc's electric razor. I'd love to take a shower, but I'm afraid somebody may knock on the door. Anyway, I'm shaving there and I'm thinking about that nice den across the hall and how I used to like to go deer-hunting and it clicks in my head and if the doc's a hunter, he's got to have some guns around here. So, back to the den, and sure enough against the wall behind the door he's got a big thing like a bookcase with glass doors and inside there's a bunch of rifles and shotguns. I'd love to take one of them, but I sure couldn't walk around without being noticed. There's got to be a pistol around here, but where? I look at the cabinet with the rifles and it has a base about six inches high and I'm thinking there's gotta be a drawer there. I put my fingers under the edge and pull and nothing happens : it's solid. I'm just about to smash it with one of the rifles when I try feeling under the edges on both sides. There's a nail or something sticking out and it moves and the whole front of the thing comes out a little. I pull and there's a big drawer chock full of rifle bullets and shotgun shells and a long-barrel twenty-two pistol wrapped in a greasy rag. I find a wood box with a big nickel-plated revolver in it, and a black leather holster with a thirty-eight automatic, which I take and put in my pocket with an extra loaded magazine.

So now I'm ready to go to New York and things look better. All I got to do is get downtown to the train station. I'm walking down the stairs and I get a big jolt of pain in my shoulder that almost knocks me on my ass. It's been hurting all along, but I guess I been so busy I didn't notice or maybe the shock of being cut has gone away. Whatever it is, I got to get some painkillers. So, I go back to the doc's office and he's still in dreamland and I start looking through his boxes and bottles of pills and junk. I pass up the tranquilizers and the phenobarbital and I come to a big plastic jar marked 'Codeine Phosphate USP – 30 mg. tabs.' I grab a large handful of the pills and put 'em in an envelope and into my jacket pocket. I remember codeine from the prison hospital, a favorite painkiller. I don't know how many to take, but one of the old orderlies in the joint told me one time that any size pill you come across is safe to take at least three a day. If they wasn't safe they wouldn't make them that size. So, I pour myself a glass of water from a jug on the doctor's little table and take two codeines. Then I head out the back door, and I check the garage right beside the house. Sure enough the doctor's car is sitting there, a big Buick. For a minute I'm thinking that would be a much easier way to get to New York than the damn train but then I drop the idea. Soon as the doctor wakes up and gets sprung I'm sitting in a hot car. He's going to call the cops and give them a story and they put out an all-points on me and the Buick.

I leave Dr Jacobson's house and start walking down the street looking for a taxi or a place to call one from. And I'm considering what I got to look forward to. If I need help from the government, they're going to turn the other way. I mean it's obvious, no matter which way I turn I got no friends on the wrong side of the fence and I got no friends on the right side of the fence. Where am I? I'm walking a tightrope which has got no end to it. Do I have to stay on this tightrope for the rest of my life? What's the sense of living? I feel as though I really would like to go to Brooklyn with my gun, and just blast everybody I could get my hands on that done me harm and just keep going, till they get me and that's the end of it. I'm really not trying to sound like James Cagney or anyone like that, but if they were around I'd start shooting at them. No way I could control myself, because I'm in a fit right now. I swear to God I don't even need a gun now with the frame of mind that I'm in.

And Butch isn't the only one. Hey, I've been pushed around by everyone, I've been shot, I've been beat up, I've been punched in the face by marshals. I've been lied to, I've been used, I've been squeezed like an orange, all the juice right out of me. They gave me the shaft all along. Yeah, one of the marshals kicked the shit out of me right after the FBI turned me over to them. I got in an argument with this guy over security. They had no guards outside the door and I tell the guy I think he's in the bag and he's six different kinds of cocksucker and next thing I know he's slapped cuffs on me and he's yelling, 'I don't have to take this shit!' And he smashes me a few in the face. I told Mister Oakes I fell in the bathtub. I was being a standup guy, because I saw it like it was part of keeping my word to them. I expected them to keep theirs but they didn't. They told me they'd arrange for me to be with Nancy after the trial but they never done it. And I had to go along with them or they'd put me in jail. It was as simple as that.

# CHAPTER FIVE

I can't stop picturing Butch sitting up in his fancy apartment fooling around with tomatoes, gambling, enjoying himself, with a ton of money and all the protection that New York City can provide. And I'm on the run with a hole through me after working on the docks and all that shit. I know the doctor will call New York when he wakes up. He has to do it and then Butch will know how bad I'm hurt, and the word will be out to all mob doctors in the East to keep an eye out for me. So I decide that if I'm going to have any chance to make it, I'll have to move against him on my own. Butch'll never suspect me of coming after him with a slug through me. I know where Butch lives in Brooklyn and I also know he probably won't have any guards around his home. He'll figure I just might make a try for the money, but he knows I'm too square to break the rules and try to hit a man in his own house.

So, I go into a diner and I call a taxi to take me to the train station in downtown Trenton. I'm going to New York to get the bastard. The thing you got to believe is that I'm two-thirds crazy right now to even try to get Butch. Because going to New York is the dumbest thing that anybody in the whole world could do. When I get there, the best thing I can do if I get lucky is to shoot Butch and try to get away. I should forget it, but I feel in my heart that I got to go. I spent so many nights in the can imagining, 'Boy, if I find out who turned me in and I get my hands on him, what I'll do to him. I'll rip the skin off his frigging back inch by inch, the son-of-a-bitch. I'll take his eyes out, bite him in the throat, and suck his

blood – *ye telo zhonga* – that means 'give me your blood.'
It's an old Sicilian expression. When we get mad at someone, really mad, we want to bite him in the throat and we
say, 'Let me get at your throat. I want to suck the blood
out of your veins.' It's a very dirty thing to say. It comes
from the old suspicions about vampires. Sicilians are very
traditional people, and in the Old Country it's almost like
a religion to be killed by another Mafioso and to die like
a man – to know you're going to die and not run from it.
Now, your real old-time Siciliano won't beg; he'll look
you right in the eye and maybe spit at you, which means a
lot because when you're real scared you don't usually have
anything in your mouth to spit.

A Sicilian kills with class – with a knife. Or an icepick.
They kill with things that are very, very quiet. I'm talking
about real Sicilians in the Old Country. When they get
through hitting you, mister, you don't even know you've
been hit. You're just laying there nice and dead in a pool
of blood and not a sound has been made. That's from the
old-timers. Today? Forget about it. You see, the old-
timers actually believed that there was some kind of religion in killing somebody. They used to take their bullets
and rub garlic all over them before they inserted them into
the pistol. And they used to put garlic on the lead balls in
their shotguns. They called the shotgun *el lupo,* which
means a wolf, and that means it's going to kill you. They
want you to know that they're going to kill you, in the Old
Country. It's not because they're looking to scare you to
death, but because they feel it's the manly thing to do, so
their enemies can protect themselves.

Most of the time in this country you hit quick when
they're not looking for it. But the old-fashioned way still
happens. I remember about five years ago there was this
one kid named Andy that we took out in the woods, and
said, 'Look, you got to go, why not let me hit you right
in the heart and you won't feel a thing.' Andy said, 'I'm

innocent, Johnny. But if you got to do it, do it.' And he turned his head away so I hit him in the heart and it went right through him. Now you got to respect a fella who acts that way. It means he's a real man and he ain't going to slobber and cry. He knows he's going to get it and he says to do it clean.

Now the taxi pulls up to the station and with all the agony I'm in I get out and walk up to the ticket counter and ask for a ticket to Penn Station, New York. And the guy's looking at me because my eyes are very, very heavy from the codeine and I'm trying not to make it obvious that I'm in pain, but I can't help myself. I'm squinting my eyes and the man says, 'Are you all right? Can I help you out?'

'I'm okay. Mind your own business and give me the ticket, that's the only way you can help me.' I'm abrupt with him because all I can think of is the pain. So I get this ticket and I edge over away from the counter and to the side of the waiting room and I'm trying to walk straight so that no one will see me favouring one side because someone might call the cops. Maybe a cop will notice and come over and shake me down, see if I'm all right, and goodbye, the game is over. So, I get to waiting around there and I decide to try and call Mister Oakes again. I don't need his help, but that other jerk, Jones, will spill that I called and I don't want to leave Mister Oakes with his mitts down. I get into a phone booth and remember he's in Rockville, Maryland, and the book says it's code 301 and I call information and I get the number and I wish I could write it down, but I got no pencil, so I think about it for a minute and try and remember it and then dial his house while it's clicking I'm thinking that a telephone booth was always a good place to catch a guy. He got no room to pull a gun or move out of the way. Now the phone's ringing, and he picks it up.

'Mister Oakes?'

'Johnny! For chrissake, where are you?'

'I called you today and got Jones, and—'

'I know about that, John.' He sounds pissed off. 'Listen, I know you broke parole. Now, if you turn yourself in—'

'I can't do that, Mister Oakes.' I say quick. And, you know, I really want to. I really do. It's good to hear his voice.

And, he's saying, 'I give you my word of honor that I'll go to bat for you. I'll tell them you were forced to run for your life.'

'No,' I says. 'I don't trust anybody but you anymore.'

'You've often told me you trust me,' he says, 'Now, why don't you come in?'

'I can't. I just can't. I believe you, Mister Oakes. But you can't promise me for them. They don't keep their word.' And it's almost out of my mouth to tell him that I can't come in because I'm on my way to kill Butch, but I don't say it – who knows, the damn line could be bugged – and he don't ask. Finally, Oakes says, 'Okay, John. I got to put this in my report first thing in the morning. That means you got about ten hours running time. And,' he says, 'I'd be careful if I was going to Boston, New York, or Baltimore. The Philly cops have been asking around if you been seen in those places. New York is real bad. I'd watch it in the bus and train stations.' And he talks to me some more about how he thinks he can get me off if I come in, that he'll swear he told me to run at the air-port for fear I'd be killed. I know Mister Oakes would say that for me. And he starts warning me that they will issue a fugitive warrant for my arrest and now the loudspeaker is beginning to hum and I know they're going to call the train and he'll hear it, so I hang up. And then the train is called. They say : 'All aboard, New Brunswick, Newark, and New York . . .' And I walk down and get on the last car and sit at the end as far down as I can so that I can see everybody that comes in and out with my back up against the wall. I'm worrying sick that I'm going to fall asleep but I've got to have a little rest, so I tell the conductor as he walks by, 'Please, I might fall asleep, I've been awful sick.' I con the guy a little bit, 'Ah, would you make sure that you give me a little nudge when it's my turn to get off at Penn Station?'

And the guy says, 'Listen, it terminates in Penn Station.' The word 'termination' goes right through my head like a bell. You know, here's another guy who wants to terminate me and I laugh to myself, well not this old guy, but who knows? And the next thing you know I doze off and all that's in my mind is being caressed and held by Nancy. We're in bed in some kind of old castle or hotel and all of a sudden the door's kicked in and there's Butch and seven of his men and all I can think of is, 'Why's he doing this to me?' And, there's a shootout right there. I'm blazing away with two guns and I can't miss. I shoot them all, except Butch, and he's got no bullets left in his gun and I'm walking toward him holding my piece on him and he's smiling and backing off farther and farther and this room's so big it seems like I'm never going to get to Butch. And then he's in a corner and he can't move and I put my gun up to his face, right between the eyes and I'm pulling the trigger and waiting to see his brains blasted all over the wall and he says, 'Hey, take me with ya. My name is Frankie. I can do this and that.' And he sounds just like he did when I first knew him years ago and I can't look at him no more cause he's starting to look like a kid as I watch his face. I close my eyes and I'm pulling and pulling on the trigger and it goes on like that, and I must not of killed him because the next thing I know Nancy and I have him out in a junkyard somewhere and we're tying him to the hood of a wrecked car. There's no windshield and his head is hanging down there over the instrument panel and he can't move, but he's spitting at me and cursing me and calling me a *gornuda*. And there's a fire in the

137

yard there like hobos use and I'm gonna heat up some wire and use it on him when I see a rat run across the yard and I get an idea. I take a bag and some bones and I catch me two rats and I bring them back to the car and in the meantime Nancy finds a big, three-pound coffee can and holds it while I pound some nail holes in the top. And they're starving, these rats, they haven't eaten in days, and we get them in the coffee can and I say to Butch, 'Now, I get even, you son-of-a-bitch.' And we pull down his pants and put the can there on his stomach and the rats are running around and he's laughing, they're tickling him. And he's saying, 'Johnny, for the love of God, don't do it! Dear Christ, please don't!' And I don't say nothing, I just tape the can down, so's it won't fall off him. And I go over to the fire and get a couple of hot coals and put them on top of the can there and he's pleading with me, 'Johnny, please shoot me, but don't do this to me. Don't!' Well, it takes a while, but the heat gets through and pretty soon the rats start to bite him. They're trying to get away from the heat and they got only one way to go – down. And he's yelling louder and louder and crying with the pain and the blood is coming out from under the can, just a trickle, you know, running down onto the hood of the car. So I go to the fire, and push around with a stick and get a real big coal and I bring it over and he sees me coming and he's screaming, 'I didn't do it! I didn't mean to do it! On my mother, he made me do it!' And I try to stop what I'm doing and it's like I can't stop. I put the big coal on the can and bend over and blow on it to make it burn hot and the rats are going crazy now; I can hear them squeaking and Butch is screaming. He can't get his breath he's screaming so loud and there's foam around his mouth and the blood's squirting now and the rats . . .

And then, I feel someone shaking me and I go right away for my gun. It's the conductor and he says, 'What's the matter? Take it easy.' You know, he don't see the gun but he can see that I'm waking up startled and he says, 'You're going to be getting off in a few minutes.' And that's the first time I really smile in a few days because that dream was so pleasant that I am thinking about doing it that way in real life. All I want to do is to get Butch and knock him off and that's the end of it. I can't think of anything else. I'm obsessed, the thought of getting away now with Nancy's even gone now. There's really nothing on my mind but revenge. And then I sit up. Jesus! What a jerk I am to sleep all the way. Mister Oakes as much as told me that the cops Butch owns are looking for me, and they're going to cover the station for sure. I could have jumped out in the Jersey marshes and come in on a truck or something. Now we're almost in Penn Station and that could really be the end of the line. I'm looking out the window now, trying to think of something, and it's like an underground railroad yard out there – empty train cars, guys working under lights, dark as a coal mine. So I get up and walk halfway to the front of the car, making like I'm looking for something I lost, and the train stops and everyone is piling off and I'm down between a couple seats looking around on the floor. And a conductor comes through the car and tells me I got to go and I do, but slow. I get outside and I'm way behind the crowd and this donkey's behind me, so I walk towards the escalator and I pass a big freight elevator. I duck around it and wait till the conductor passes me, and then start back to the other end of the platform. I get to the end, but it's so black down there I can't see a thing. I know it's no more than five feet down to the tracks but I don't want to break a leg. So I get down on my knees and go over the edge like it was a wall, holding on to the top with my hands. And, I'm standing there a minute getting used to the dark, and a train comes in a few tracks away and I can see by the light it throws that there's a wall to this tunnel maybe eight tracks away. Now, I got a problem. It's midnight or after and I can't go looking for Butch right now. He's somewhere doing business and with other guys or he's with a girl and I don't know where that is. I know he's not going to be home until morning. So I got to spend the next six hours off the street. I don't want to chance any flophouses or motels so maybe the best thing for me is to flop right here in the dark and hope that the railroad cops are fucking off at this hour. Anyway the train passes and I start walking across the tracks, keeping an eye on the third rails that got wood guards on top of them. I'm against the wall of the tunnel in a couple of minutes and I start to walk back away from the station. There's all kinds of crap piled against the wall and a bare light bulb every thirty feet. There's piles of sand and piles of rails and little barrels of spikes and then there's a stack of dirty sandbags between two lights. I climb on top of the pile and lie down and I'm out. The next thing I know I hear a screeching sound and I sit up and there's a train three or four tracks away that's coming in and full of people so it's got to be early in the morning. I feel shitty as hell, but I know I got to get out of here. So, I get down off of the sandbags and start walking. It seems like I've gone half a mile when I come to a set of iron steps and I go up, figuring there has to be a way for these guys down here to get out in case of fire. I get up to the top and there's a little platform and an iron door in the wall. I turn the knob and pull it – and nothing, it don't budge. I try pushing and it gives a little and I put my shoulder to the door and she opens hard and noisy and there's cold air on my face. I come out in a little six-foot tunnel and I walk out and I'm on Thirty-Third Street, outside the big post office and across from a YMCA. I'm more than a block from the railroad station and no one in the world's going to know I was on that train.

Now I put my hand underneath my coat and it feels wet and comes out with blood all over. I got to get the hell to some kind of doctor that can help me, but before I do this I got to get to this bastard. I look up at the big clock and its eight-oh-five in the morning and I'm thinking about taking the subway, but it's too long. I'm saying to myself, 'I'll never stay on my feet that long. I got to get this done before I pass out.' So, I get in a cab and give the driver the address and I keep trying to shade my head and stay awake because right now I've been gulping pills. They're not working too good because I'm becoming immune to them : all they're doing is putting me to sleep. I know this is dumb, so I take out a cigarette and light up and burn my finger doing it, which wakes me up a little. Then I burn myself again, this time with the cigarette on the back of my hand. I'm sitting here trying to figure out what Butch knows and how close he is to grabbing me. By this time, the doctor must have called in, so Butch knows I got a few hundred bucks, a suit and a gun. He knows I'm hurt pretty bad so he's going to have all the mob doctors in New York staked out just in case I show up. But, I'm thinking, wait a minute, Doc Jacobson's also going to tell Butch I overheard the call to his office, so I know they got the mob doctors covered and I'm not going near another one. He'll have to play it safe, but he will guess that I might try the emergency ward of some hospital. With the bullet out of me, no doctor is going to have to report me to the cops. I can tell them it's some other kind of wound. So Butch will get his bagmen to check the likely hospitals. He's got all kinds of medical connections, you know. Years ago, he figured out how to find a certain guy we was looking for because he knew the guy's wife had a certain blood disease and she had to have these special shots every week or two. So, Butch figures there can't be that many women answering her description who got the same disease and he tells a couple of mob doctors to find the lady. Took two, three weeks and they found her. All they did was call hospitals and medical groups

in the likely part of the country and they give them a
story that this lady is a former patient of theirs who left
no forwarding address but who might have developed
complications that her new doctor don't know about, and
they are very concerned about her health. Also, they are
a little pissed that the lady may have run off without paying all her doctor bills. It worked like a charm. So Butch
knows I'm not going near any mob doctors or hospitals,
which leaves regular doctors or Nancy, my *goumara*,
who's pretty good with bandages. He's going to cover
her and he's going to cover the bank. Why else would I
take a chance, coming to New York?

Now, the neighborhood is beginning to look familiar.
It's a good half-hour drive out to this part of Brooklyn,
and the cab fare comes to twenty-two dollars because it's
a pretty good haul. But with the price of cabs today in New
York, that's not a lot of money. So I pay the cabbie and
the driver says, 'Hey, something wrong with you, pal?'
because he sees that I'm bouncing off walls, you know, I
can't even keep my eyes open. I can hardly stand up
straight.

'No, there's nothing wrong with me,' I say. 'I had a
little bit too much to drink last night and I've got a hang-
over.' So I have the driver take me past Butch's house and
I get down in the seat so no one inside can see me. It's a
two-story brick with a driveway on the right and a lot
of trees and bushes and I can't see no car there and I say
to myself, 'The bastard's still out, or he's already left.' I
don't know, so I get the guy to circle around and I get out
a block and a half from Butch's place. It's a shifty day.
It's been raining and the street is wet. I'm out there on
the sidewalk and I start moving in what I hope is the right
direction. I'm trying to walk so I won't attract attention,
like a guy who's getting home very, very late after drinking all night. Anybody says hello I'm going to tell them
I left my taxi a block from home so I can sneak in and not

wake the wife. And there's some people on the street – school kids, a guy leaving for work late, a delivery truck dropping off something. Now, I see Butch's house and there's no car in front, but it could be in the driveway and he could of come home in the last five minutes without me seeing him.

Main thing is I got to pay attention in case he just drives past me while I'm walking along here. He does that and he'll make me right off the bat. So what do I do? Start walking up the path of the house I'm in front of? Go for the nearest car and make like I'm getting in? Maybe somebody in the house thinks I'm stealing it. Do I fall down and hide under the bushes? Behind a tree? What? I'm feeling out in the open here, like anyone can spot me. Maybe Butch warned the whole neighborhood to be on the lookout for his old friend – 'You see Forza, shoot him ...? But this is a laugh, because Butch keeps a very low profile out here at home. We all do, you know. You ever read about a mob guy getting whacked out and the neighbors saying anything else but he was a good neighbor and very quiet? No one here's going to know nothing. They hear me shoot, they think it's the Fourth of July. Suddenly, I hear a car behind me in the next block and I stop in front of a tree and look back and here's this big black job coming down slow. I can't see what kind of car it is, but it could be him. So, I'm telling myself not to panic and I get to the next house with the car maybe a hundred feet behind me and I don't look back. I just turn casual and start walking up the cement to the front door. My neck is stiff and I'm walking slow motion and the car passes down the street. I stop and look like I'm dizzy, shake my head and all, and make it back to the sidewalk in time to see the car turn the next corner. And I'm relieved but still not sure it wasn't him. He could be going around just to play safe. So I'm walking faster. I want to get there before the car comes back. And I come to the house next to Butch's, a white colonial-type and there's a lot of low pine trees and high bushes there between this one and Butch. His place is only about thirty feet from this white one, but you can't see through. So I stop where the bushes are thick and I look around fast and go down in on the dirt. It's wet and muddy and I worm my way in six, ten feet and I'm going to be a real mess, but I can't be seen from the street or the house now. And I'm waiting and waiting for that car to come back around but it don't come. So that's a relief. It wasn't him – or maybe it was him and he spotted me and he's coming in through the back alley. I take my gun out and I hold it ready and I wait.

And I'm wondering if he's got any men spotted around. I don't think so. He has no reason to have any guards around the house. He wouldn't be expecting anything here. So I'm saying to myself that I shouldn't be here, but it don't make sense that I should hang around near his office or at a certain restaurant at three o'clock, because then there's going to be piles of people there, all kinds of mob guys. This is the only shot I'm ever going to get at him alone. That's why I'm here. Like the time Butch and I hit Taglonetti in front of his girl's house. I wonder if Butch remembers Louis. I wonder if he ever looks at the bushes and thinks that somebody could be out here laying for him. But Butch knows I stick pretty much to the rules – not sucker-straight, but by the rules covering men that are made. So maybe I surprise him. He'd figure I only come out here to whack him if I already tried finding him alone everyplace else. But wait a minute, I'm thinking he knows I haven't had a chance to tail him so I might come here direct. Except for one thing – I am not a guy that was always thinking about revenge, and he knows that, and that I do need the stash. So Butch is not going to think of me out here, at least not right now. Not yet. It's starting to rain and I'm pushing deeper under the trees, not that

I can really stay dry, but – Ohhh, shit! I hit my head on something pushing through there. And I can see it now, a metal stake with a wire through a hole on top and now I can see another one about six feet away. I don't think it's an alarm, just a marker between the houses. I don't think Butch has any alarms. Mister Butch is riding on top of the world these days and thinks he's never going to get it because he's so smart that he gets anyone first who might be thinking the wrong thing. So why would he have his house wired?

After sitting what I think is forever I get my gun out to make sure there's bullets in it, and so forth. I'm wondering how long I can last out here if he is home, but there's no physical evidence that he's around; I don't hear anything or see his car. But maybe the son-of-a-bitch lent the car to someone or it's in for service. I don't know, maybe he's even got a different car by now. And now I'm thinking about Butch's habits: like Butch knows my habits, I know his. I'm saying to myself, 'Well, this bum has got to come home.' He always does, because he wants to take a shower and clean up, change his clothes. Like any wiseguy he's been out most of the night and he spent time with some girl and now he comes home to get ready for the day. But Butch is a little different. He never did marry because he was too full of ambition. He used to say, 'You can't be married, be happy, and be a success.' He likes to have a woman sent up when he feels like it and outside of that he don't want to have to put up with one. So Butch bought the house out here for his mother and older sister and they keep it for him. He has a place in town for entertaining, but he looks on this as home. I'm remembering the times I was here before, though there weren't so many in the last few years. He'd have his two uncles and their families over and his married sister and her husband and kids and his mother's cousin from New Jersey, and there'd be Butch at the table making like an Italian papa. The

145

only trouble was he really didn't enjoy it. He hated kids and before supper was over he'd leave and say he had business to take care of. And if I was there we'd drive back to Manhattan and grab a couple of girls and bounce around the clubs for a while.

If he's in this house right now, Butch's habit is to come out of the house by nine-thirty, because then he's either picked up or he drives himself. At ten-fifteen him and the bosses and his runners and everyone else sit down in a restaurant and have breakfast and discuss the day's business — what's going to take place in loan-sharking, who's bookmaking this week, and any other mob business. And all I can think of is I don't give a damn how long I got to wait here but just let me stay awake, stay conscious long enough.

But now it gets into my head that what I just said about Butch and his habits is all wrong. Sure, that's his habits on any *regular* day. But this isn't a regular day for him. He hasn't had many regular days since I turned and he got the action to whack me out. Ever since, and even more since the government dropped me, he spends a lot of time on Johnny Forza. He knows that I'm circling the stash like a fly around honey. So, who knows when he's coming home? He's maybe been up all night making sure the bank is covered and checking, checking, checking to see if he can find where the hell I am or how I slipped through or if I'm somewhere else. But, I don't like to think this way because it means he may not be coming home at all today. Maybe he's snoozing on the couch in his office over that garage on the West Side. Maybe he's in his apartment getting ready to go back to the office. And maybe I'm out here in all this shit for nothing.

So I make up my mind I'm going to stop all these kind of ideas. And I close my eyes and decide that I'm going to grab him and put my gun in his mouth and blow his head off. When I do it, I'll have to bury him or dump him in the ocean or something so he's never found because if he is found the cops will come to me because I used to hang around with him. If his body disappears they could never find who done it, but when a body shows up there could be identifying situations – the way he was tied up, the way he was hit, the bullet he was hit with, things like that. A lot of times you bury a guy not to get the other mob guys mad at you, not to get the police mad at you, not to get associations, and so forth.

I'm keeping my head busy with this crap while I sit here catching pneumonia. All I can really think of now is that I'm wet and cold and that Butch would be laughing if he knew I was here and he's there. And I can feel myself getting mad and I'm ready to stand up and get the hell out. Go over to Manhattan and look for the son-of-a-bitch. Go to his apartment. Go to the office. And I'm starting to turn around so I can get out of this place when I hear a car. I'm down in the mud and I look out under the bushes, and sure enough, here comes a big black Lincoln up the street. He's still got it, the son-of-a-bitch, and all of a sudden the pain in me goes away. I don't feel it anymore. What I do feel is dizzy and sick, probably from all this codeine that I stole from the doctor. I'm junked up high as a kite. I don't know whether I'm coming or going, but I know that this creep is driving up in his goddamn Lincoln and I'm going to blow his brains out. I'm looking at the car and I don't even know whether it's Butch in there. The guy looks like Butch, but it's raining. Even though he's only about thirty feet away I don't know for sure so I'm staring, squinting my eyes, watching him and the door opens and his head pops out – and it's Butch. And the bastard's dressed like always, like he just got out of church – gray suit, white shirt, gray tie, and a topcoat that matches the suit. He's got a hat on and he looks at his watch and I can almost see the diamonds in it all the way over here.

I'm thirty to forty feet away from him – a hell of a shot for a thirty-eight, which is what I've got. Well, I'm so anxious, I get the gun out and he's on the other side of the car and I stand up and think I better circle him and get closer and he walks around to the rear of the car. He don't see me yet. I got the thirty-eight in my hand and I yell, 'Butch, you son-of-a-bitch, now I got you!' And I reach out to shoot and suddenly realize that my arm is so sore I can't hold the gun steady. So, I hold it with both hands like the cops do. And I let two or three shots go, I don't know how many. 'You son-of-a-bitch! It's me!' I'm screaming and Butch falls to the ground right next to the car, but I don't think he's hit: he just slipped. So, I jump out of the bushes to get close and finish him and I fall on my face because I'm weak as a flea. I land on the grass and come up shooting because I see Butch running like hell down the street. As fast as I can, I get into the car. I'm all out of breath, but through the fog in my head I can see that the keys are still in it. I start it up, put it into reverse, floor it and, bang, catch the fender of a car that's standing in front of the house because I can't see good and I'm going like hell and I don't stop till I smash into a car parked across the street. Now I put it into drive and I'm tearing after Butch. I've got the goddamn window open on the other side but not on my side, and I catch up to Butch a little and he's out of his topcoat and the hat's gone and for just a second I'm not sure it's him and then I am and I throw a shot at him. I only got two or three slugs left so I got to be careful now. Butch jumps behind some bushes and I lose sight of him and stop the car and get out. I go onto the sidewalk and look around the bushes and see him jump over the back fence in somebody's yard. Now I'm running over the lawn after him and I reach the fence just in time to catch him running down the alleyway, dodging around empty garbage cans, and I shoot again and then, click, I'm out of bullets. I start to climb over the fence and suddenly my shoulder is hurting again and I'm feeling very noticeable in someone's backyard, like the noise has got to wake up half the neighborhood and any second I'm going to hear the sirens coming my way. I lean against the fence for a minute and I want to cry, I want to curse God but I can't. All I can think of is that this creep is gone. I lost him and I'll never, never get another chance at him.

So I go back to the car and start going again and I drive slow. I'm cool enough not to make any more show. I know it's dynamite for me to be in this car, so I go to a section where I can park it and get lost in a crowd of people, you know what I mean, just before Main Street there. So I just pull the car over and leave the keys in the ignition.

I'm sitting here now feeling wrung out like a towel. My arm hurts and I'm tired and I look down and the car seat is covered with blood. It looks like someone killed a chicken in here. They see this and they know I'm gone and, I'm thinking, maybe I am. I get out of the car and start walking and hope I'm not dripping on the sidewalk, except with the rain it won't make no difference. I really am gone, I got about $180 and an empty gun. I'm wearing dirty clothes, and I look like a bum that's been sleeping it off in the gutter. A cop sees me now, and its maybe the drunk tank. My God! I wish Nancy was here right now. She could take me and walk me right to bed and she'd put her soft hands on me and rub away all the pain. I haven't talked to her in weeks. When they had me stashed on an Army base and it made no difference if the mob knew I was, I could call her up. Then a month ago, they smuggled me out of there and moved me around so the mob wouldn't find it so easy to whack me out and I couldn't make no calls. I pass a phone booth and I think of Nancy and I turn back and pass it again. I can feel the change in my pocket and I want to reach out and put a dime in there and just call her. I really want to talk to her so bad right now, but can I take the chance? They got her phone covered for sure. And I'm standing here in front of this phone booth staring at it and the door is like a fence that Butch has put up to keep us apart. I call her and they can't trace the call so easy, but they know that whatever I say or don't say, we're going to meet, so they follow her wherever she goes and she leads them to me. 'Hey, mister!' I turn fast and it's a guy in a blue sweatshirt, 'You waiting for a call?'

'Nah,' I say and walk away from the phone booth. And I'm passing another booth now and I think, what if I call her and just don't saying nothing, just listen to her voice? I'd love to hear it right now, hear her say, 'Hello, honey. Hi there, babe.' Or just, 'Hello.' Anything. But I can't call and not talk to her. I think if I hear her voice I'm going to be so glad that I can't help myself from talking and telling her how much I love her and how I missed her all this time and how I need her now.

I go into a bar, a dark place so they won't see how dirty I am, and I slap five on the wood and ask for a shot of rye and a glass of water and I head for the men's room. Place is empty and I run water on my face and comb my hair and stuff a handful of paper towels under my shirt to try and sop up the blood. I come back to the bar, toss down the shot, order another, and go to the phone booth in the back. Inside, I hold the book up to the little light and turn to the 'O' pages and then find the names beginning with 'One' and then 'One Hundred' and finally I come to it, it's right there, One Hundred Eighty-One East Sixty-Seventh Street. And I read the number and put the dime in and call Nancy's building. It rings and rings and rings and a man answers.

'Is this one-eight-one east sixty-seventh?'

'Yes, sir. This is O'Malley. I'm on the door.'

'This is Mister Martin. I'm Nancy Martin's uncle and I'm trying to get to her.'

'Yes, sir.'

'Listen, Miss Martin's phone don't answer. Would you buzz her and tell her to come down and call me. It's important. Very important.' And the guy is nice as pie and I read him the number of the phone booth. I know Nancy chucks the doorman under the chin every time she goes out and he's crazy about her. He tells me he'll get her right down right away and he's sure she's home because he ain't seen her go out. I hang up and pick up my second rye and come back to the phone. And the minutes pass – five, six minutes. Ten minutes and I'm wondering if maybe she's out or in the shower or the doorman is in the bag and got to give the man on the wiretap time to hook onto the lobby phone. Maybe the guy give him the number I'm calling from and they're checking it out.

The phone rings.

I grab it so fast I drop it and hit my head on the door picking it up, and she says, 'Baby! How are you? Are you okay?' And I'm laughing. Relieved. 'Hey, Nancy!' And I can hardly talk. I got no breath all of a sudden. And she's saying, 'Take it easy, babe. Nancy's right here.'

'Oh, Nancy! God, it's good to hear you. I missed you so much and I couldn't call.'

'Johnny, baby. I love you.'

And, I'm sitting there just feeling good, warm for a change and I remember where she is and I say, 'Listen, Nancy, your Aunt Sara has been very, very sick. She has lead poisoning.'

'Oh, my God.'

'So, I think you ought to try and see her right away. She's staying at that nice place you used to visit with her in the summer.'

'Oh,' she says, 'please tell Aunt Sara I love her and she'll be in my prayers.'

I hang up the phone, pick my change off the bar, and go out and flag down the next taxi and get in and I'm thinking that when the cops come to investigate this shooting and they'll find Butch's car and my fingerprints are everywhere. The thing is: who's going to find the car? I don't know whether it'll be the cops or Butch or if it's even going to be stolen from the place I just parked it. That would be a help. The thief might leave plenty of his own prints, or wipe the car down or maybe repaint it and then they'll never find it again. I know if Butch gets it there's going to be no sweat, but if it's the cops . . . And then I'm saying to myself, 'Fuck the damn car! Who gives a shit about who finds it?' I must of said it out loud because the driver turns and says, 'Huh?' Thing is, the cops are going to be after me pretty soon anyway, just like Mister Oakes said. I think I been on the run too long. I'm turning into a rat, you know, always sneaking around, scared and jumpy, worried over everything. Right now, the only thing that matters is connecting up with Nancy. I'm still feeling warm from talking to her. I can hardly wait to grab her and hold her and I'm going to do that, busted wing or no. Jesus! It's been a long time. And I'm smiling because I might have thought of a trick that Butch didn't figure on. If he don't know I called, then it's going to be easier for her to get out and meet me without being tailed.

I can feel myself getting mad again. I'm tired of all this running and hiding. I want to fight. I want to fight them all and the hell with it. It'd be the easiest thing in the world for me to cut out right now and go somewhere like Wisconsin and wind up milking cows. No one'd ever find me. But I can't do it that way. I got to fight to have what's mine, and I got to get back at Butch. I got to get Nancy and everything I had and then turn around and tell them, 'Hey, you thought you got the best of me? Well, you didn't. I won, I got the best of you!'

So the cab is almost there and I stop him and get out near the parking lot like I'm going to pick up my car.

And I'm right across the street from Nathan's on Surf Avenue in Coney Island. Nathan's is a beat-up hotdog stand that's been out here for a million years. Looks like skid row but the hot dogs is the best there is. Nancy and me used to sneak out here once in a while during the day and we'd go on the rides and feed the goats and pigs in the little animal zoo round the corner and act like suckers. Go down to the aquarium and watch them feed the fish. Go out on the pier and watch the fishermen. I always felt the only time we could ever be ourselves was when we was alone and that meant being someplace not first-class. You see, all the places people go for fun – restaurants, hotels, resorts, whatever – if they're plush the mob has got a piece of it or if they don't they will. And those are the places that wiseguys go. So this was our special place because it's not plush and we'd never meet anyone who knew us. I'd take my tie off and leave my coat in the car and she'd tone it down a little just so we wouldn't stand out, and we'd do the boardwalk. I remember winning a big blue stuffed bear for her one summer by throwing baseballs at those iron milk bottles they have. I was trying for the big box of chocolates. She's still got that damn bear. She keeps it in her bedroom and says it looks like me.

I been here fifteen minutes now and I wish the hell she'd hurry and get here. I start wondering if maybe they followed her and she's trying to shake them or if they grabbed her – and I'm not going to think that way no more. The truth is she's probably taking time to get dressed. Not dressed up, dressed down. Nancy's a tall, five-nine blonde and her figure is out of sight, believe me. When we walked into a place everybody just stared at her. Used to get under my skin, see because she's younger than me. But, as beautiful as she is, and everything else, she's got smarts. When you don't want to stand out she'll tone it down and she better if she's going to be with me. I'm wearing the clothes I took off the doc and they're a mess. Not like the suits I used to get made by that guy down on Broadway. His clothes were fantastic, started off at five, five-fifty a suit and go up to eight hundred and better. And he'd always do a matching topcoat in the same material, and when I'd buy the outfit I'd say, 'I want a hat to match,' and they'd make a hat for me, for my face. I mean the size of the brim would be just right. I got a big face and the brim would be a little wider than the next guy. And shoes, I had thirty, forty pairs at all times and they was – wait a minute. There's a five-, six-year-old black Plymouth coming up the street slow. It stops across from me. Window comes down and – it's Nancy. She's waving at me. I throw my cigarette and get over there fast as I can move. Up close she looks different. Younger. Different but beautiful. She opens the door and gets out and I come up to the car and she's standing there looking and she runs at me and grabs me around the neck and she's crying and I'm holding her and trying not to fall. My arm hurts like fire.

'Oh, babe,' she says. 'Babe. Babe. What did they do to you?' And she's kissing me on the face and the neck and I want to hold her up in the air like I do, but I can't do it.

'Ah, it's nothing. I got a little hole in me. Don't worry about it.'

So, we get in the car and I look at her and, like I figured, she's in disguise, wearing loafers and a pair of not tight, but very good-fitting, blue jeans and a jean jacket and a little sweater. Instead of wearing her hair up, she's got it down and pulled back in a pony tail like a hippie kid. No earrings and sunglasses that don't show her beautiful blue eyes. Very plain. And the car's the same, a disguise. One she bought for lamming. Kept it parked in a building a block and a half from where she lives. So she gets my call, changes clothes, and instead of going down under her own building and driving out in her blue Camaro, she walks out pulling one of them grocery carts like she's going to the supermarket. And she goes a couple of blocks, ducks into this other building and downstairs and into the Plymouth, and she's gone. On the way out here she keeps circling to see if they're onto her and she don't think so. And now she's driving around Coney Island doing the same thing. She keeps turning, this way, that way, the other way, you know, use the turn light and then don't make a turn, park fast and wait, all the tricks I taught her to spot a tail. And I say to myself, 'Why would they be tailing us? If they'd seen me get in the car, they'd have forced it off the road by now.' They would have shot us both and it would have made the papers as one more 'gangland execution'. So I tell Nancy to take a right and go past Sheepshead Bay and see if she can find us a no-name motel around where they got all those yacht clubs on the other side of Shore Parkway. I just can't believe we're here together and Butch don't know where we are. The best damn thing I done today was to get to her before he got the word out. I bet there's a gang of his people around her building right now. And I'm laughing and Nancy turns and makes a kiss with her mouth and I smile at her and I can feel myself fading, going under. I know why. I'm with her now and I'm feeling a little safe for a minute and so I'm letting go, not holding on the way I been holding for the past couple days. Anyway, I told Nancy to find a little motel because I think Butch will figure we'll head out in the country, not too far away, so I can find a doctor. You know, someplace like the Catskills, Montauk, or the Jersey shore, where we can lay low for a while and then come back and make a try for the stash. So we don't do that, you see? And Nancy drives into the parking lot of a motel, a little place looks like a marina, and she goes inside to register and I watch her cute ass as she walks over there and I'm closing my eyes.

The car door opens and Nancy's leaning in and she helps me out of the car. She makes sure no one's looking, opens the door to the room. And we go in and I just fall on the bed. She locks the door and puts the chain on and then she comes over and tries to make me comfortable by taking my jacket off. Now I'm in agony. My eyes are just about closing and she opens up my jacket and sees nothing but a mass of bloody bandages. I'm sopping with blood all over my clothes and everything. So she takes my clothes off as best she can and she goes in and gets towels out of the bathroom and starts cleaning me up and she says, 'Johnny,' and I'm out.

'Johnny! Johnny!' I hear her yelling, 'Johnny! Wake up!' and I'm half gone now so she says, 'I got to go to the drugstore and get some disinfectant and stuff before you get gangrene.'

'Don't leave me,' I'm really scared to be here on my back and alone.

'I have to leave you for a little while,' she says.

'Please! Nancy, please!' I'm begging her. I can't sit up. I can hardly move now and I'm cold. I don't want to die here alone. And I'm scared Butch'll come crashing in the door and he's going to cut me into little pieces and she won't be here. She puts her hand on my face and I grab it and hold on. I won't let her go.

The next thing I know, Nancy's shaking me awake again. She's got a whole bag of stuff like Bactine and cotton and bandages and tape, plus she's bought a couple of cups of coffee which she thinks might wake me up. So she washes me and cleans me and she's talking all this time, 'Ohhh, Jesus!' and 'Honey, this is going to hurt.' And she pours something on and I can't feel nothing except maybe a little warmer. I'm really half out of it and she tussels with me, pushing me around, big heavy man, you know. Finally, she gets me bandaged and she's killing herself trying to get me in a position in bed where I'll be halfways comfortable. And I hear her from far away, 'John, my love. I can't take this. I'm supposed to pretend, I know, but . . .' Anyway, she gets me set and my legs up on the bed and I can hear her crying and I'm out like a light.

She tells me later that I was moaning and groaning and she crawled in beside me and tried to soothe me. Anyway, we pass the night somehow and I wake up about seven in the morning and look over at her and say, 'Thanks,' because I know I couldn't have made it through the night without her. She moves over and puts her head on my chest. It hurts, but I don't tell her. 'Oh, John.' She's running her hand down my side. I reach over and touch her hair. 'John, it's been so long. I missed you so much.'

'I know. I know. Me too.'

'Not knowing was the worst thing.'

'I know.' Her head is up now and she moves up and kisses me and touches the shoulder and sees me flinch. 'Oh, babe. I'm sorry.' She sits up. 'I forgot—' I smile at her and reach out with my left hand and she grabs it and kisses it. 'Oh, John. You were so bad last night I was scared I'd have to call a doctor and—'

'Yeah,' I say, trying to sound strong, 'but you didn't and now I'm pretty good.' I'm feeling not bad, but weak. 'You know, you're a real nurse.' And she smiles and I know she wants to hear what happened. Now, one of the rules is you tell your wife nothing, but this don't apply to the *goumara*. She's around when you're making deals you don't want to talk about at home. So the girl always knows more than the wife. She has to – it's part of the reason you got her, so you'd have someone you could open up with. 'Number one, Nancy, the government dropped me three days ago. Number two—'

'Dropped you?' She's not smiling now. 'What does that mean?'

'It means they dropped me. No more protection. No money. Nothing.'

'But, they promised—'

'Sure. Promises, promises. When it comes time to deliver, forget it.' I don't tell her they think I blew the case.

'But can they do that?'

'Anything,' I say. 'They can do anything they want. Send me back to the can. Anything.' And she's sitting there shaking her head. She really don't believe it. So I tell her, 'Look, number one, they dropped me. Number two, one of Butch's people took a shot at me day before yesterday because I'd been dropped and had no marshals around.' I figure I tell her the details later on. 'Anyway, Nancy, what you don't know is that Butch put the finger on me.' You see, I never told her my suspicions.

And Nancy says, 'You must know, honey, but I can't believe it – I mean you grew up together – that he would do this to you.'

'Well, I narrowed it down,' I says, 'and there's no one else possible but him and the Old Man who could have done this to me. Just the two of them. And I don't believe that the Old Man done it purposely. Butch is the son-of-a-bitch, he's been treacherous all his life.'

Now, Nancy'd met Butch and the Old Man on many occasions, but she never got to know them well. When she was still working in this nightclub and I call her over and the Old Man is there and a few other people and I'd say, 'You people all know Nancy?'

'How are you?' and 'Sit down, won't you?' They all smile at her, she sits down and she don't overdrink because I wouldn't be able to get involved with her. She's got to know when to talk and when not to – with mob guys, you know, keep her mouth shut most of the time. She's got to be able to sit there and maybe hear a little cursing going on at the table without sticking her nose up in the air. She's got to have brains. If not, they'd tell me right off the bat, 'Dump her.' And she knows this. I think she always knew this.

'I should have realized that he was treacherous then,' I tell her.

'But you and Butch always got along so good.'

'Yeah, but things change. He's power hungry.' And I explain to her that while I was in jail he tried to kill me a couple of times. Nancy finds this hard to believe. She can't think that the Old Man had a hand in turning me in. But there's no reason she should. I never told her about things like that before. The thing is, she has the idea that the public has got of mob guys – that they'll walk through coals rather than give up one of their friends. They talk about the informer that they think is no good and they say, 'Well, he'd give up anybody, he'd give his mother up.' See, the public thinks this because of movies and stuff like that, but actually it isn't that way at all.

Many bosses and even underbosses give people up and never get caught. They call up their contact men at the police station, and they say, 'Look, Charlie who lives down the street hasn't been kicking in every week. I want you to raid him. Catch him cold turkey and let him go to the can.' You understand? But they're not weasels because they're the boss, they can do no wrong. But if a guy that isn't a boss does that, then he's no good, he's a stool pigeon, a rat, a fink, whatever you want to call him. And the public goes along with it. That's right – the boss is emperor, he's Caesar, he's God, he's everything. If you had a brother that done something wrong, he'd tell you, 'Go kill your brother,' and if you say no, he'll have you killed for disobeying him. This is what the bosses are. You can't win.

I'm saying all this to Nancy. I can't stop talking, but she says she's interested and she looks like she is. I just haven't had a chance to talk to anyone who wanted to hear my story and who'd believe it. 'I can just picture

Butch dropping the dime on me,' I tell her. 'He calls up his own bagman in the station, understand? He says, "Charlie, this is Butch. I want you to get some people together, go to such-and-such a street in Brooklyn. There's a warehouse garage over there. Go there at three o'clock right on the nose. And you're going to find a trailerload of missing whiskey and some people in there and you can have them."

'The guy's going to say, "Who's the people?"

' "The guy is Johnny Forza, couple other bums. You work for me? You do things my way," he's telling the cop. "Okay? I can't be involved in this at all." He hangs up and calls me, "Johnny, this is Butch. I have a chance to sell that whole load of merchandise. Got to bring the apple over here at three o'clock. Meet me there?"

' "Okay, sure." I go in. Next thing you know, at about two minutes past three, knock on the door of the warehouse. "Who is it?"

' "It's the police. Open up!"

'I say to myself I got to hide. You know, we got bagmen all over the joint. "All right, wait a minute. I'll let you in."

' "You're under arrest," they say, before they even walk in the door.

' "For what?"

' "Stolen merchandise. Got a warrant here."

' "How can you arrest me before you see if the stuff is here?" I'm a little cocky. I don't know what the score is, but I think I do. "Why don't you stay here, let me make a phone call?" I want to go to the bagman, you know?

' "You make your phone call down at the station," says the cop in charge. By this time they find the stolen whiskey and they take me downtown and book me. And they take me before a judge and the judge puts bail and who do you think comes and bails me out?'

'Gee, honey, I don't know? Was it the Old Man?' Nancy looks puzzled.

'Come on, Nancy. Who would want to bail me just to keep me in the dark?'

'Butch?'

'Right! Butch, the son-of-a-bitch! And he comes to the court and he's very concerned, "Who could have done this to you?" he's asking and, of course, I don't realize it was him that set me up.

' "Hey, by the way, Butch, I thought you were going to be there at three o'clock."

' "You know," he says, face serious, "as soon as I pulled up there I seen police cars all over the joint. I had the sucker with me and we left. I didn't want to add to it by getting in there."

'I say, "Well, you done the right thing. It's good you didn't come in, they would have arrested you, too." I'm still feeling loyal to the bastard.

'Then, I'm out on bail and I go have supper with the Old Man and Butch and a few others at Gino's, and the Old Man is very friendly and asks the old lady who cooks, "What did you make today?" And we start with some wine and antipasto and it's a good feeling. They're all great guys and they're patting me on the back :

' "Don't worry about a thing, we got lawyers working."

' "You'll be on the street before you know it."

' "It'll do you a world of good, you come back in good shape.

' "Sorry about your time, I got a friend . . ."

' "Hey, remember the old days? It'll be like that again."

'And they make it sound like I'm going off to war or something and I'm beginning to feel okay and I say, "Don't have to worry, I'll do it standing on my ear." And we eat and it's getting late and the Old Man leans over to me and asks, "John, you know who done this thing to you?"

' "I haven't the slightest idea," I said.

' "You haven't any idea?" says the *le patrone*.

' "It doesn't make any difference. Maybe they were just tailing me."

' "Well, it just seems funny they had the warrant and everything."

' "Yeah, it does seem funny, but who can we blame? *Patrone*, we can't just blame anybody that walks by because that's an awful accusation to make."

'And the Old Man says, "Okay, go to jail, because you're going to get it, there's no question about it," he says. "If you go to jail, I will take care of your properties, I will make sure that your wife has got some money. Any problems, your wife calls me. And Butch'll take care of everything for you."

'Butch says, "Oh yeah, don't worry, John, you and I been too close for all these years. I'll make sure you get what you deserve. I know where the stash is, and so forth." And he tells me on the side, "I'll also take care of Nancy."

'Then we talk business for a while and one guy says, "Hey, John, what other companies you own? We'll watch them for you," and "What cops you have that we can keep paying?" And I'm laying it all out, my book, my loan-sharking, my stuff in Manhattan, thinking these guys are my friends. But what they were really trying to find out is what they can steal when I'm gone. You see, Nancy?'

She nods, but she can't answer.

'Okay,' I tell her, 'what's done is done. I got nobody to blame but myself, I should have known—'

She says, 'But, honey, how could you know?'

'I should have known because, like I told you, I seen it happen before. I was just too high-and-mighty to think they could do it to me.' And she comes over and gives me a hug and a kiss.

162

But the fucking didn't stop at Gino's. Butch put it to me by setting me up right into the can – and then the FBI took over and got me to turn stoolie. They worked on my temper by showing me pictures of Butch's new car and pictures of him enjoying himself in Miami with some broad. And they told me, 'He's the one that turned you in.' They drove me crazy doing this. I'd go back to my cell and feel like beating my head against the wall.

'I'm sorry I didn't kill the bastard yesterday,' I tell Nancy. 'He's going to walk away in his happy way and I'm going to die.'

'No,' she says, 'we'll make a new life together after all this business.' And I'm saying to myself, 'How can we make a new life with this guy hunting me like an animal, the whole mob on me like animals?'

'Nancy,' I says, 'I got to go back. I got to see if I can take another shot at Butch.'

'Forget about it, Johnny. Forget about it,' Nancy says. 'We got to get some money and get out of here, because it's just a question of time before they spot me or you and then we'll both be pretty near dead.' And I'm thinking that one of the things Butch knows now is that I'm not as easy to figure as he thought. He didn't expect me to come after him at home. That move makes me an outlaw, a crazy cowboy. From here on, he's never going to be sure again about what I do or how I think.

I say, 'They know a lot more about me now than they did. I think it's getting too hot for us.'

'What do they know except that you shot at Butch?'

'Well,' I say to her, 'I got to figure it this way – he's alerted the whole mob that I'm in the city, and when they find that car they're going to see the blood, so they'll know I'm in bad shape. They're going to check inside where you live, and they're going to see you're not there anymore. Then they're going to put two and two together and any moron that could come up with four would know that we're with each other and that I'm hurt and they'll also know I'm packing a gun. So – they know that I'm like a rat caught in a corner right now, and if anybody spots me they're going to shoot me right there. They're not going to wait for Butch anymore; they're going to just kill me right there where they see me. And, yeah, they also know that the government don't have me under protection anymore. They know that there's no marshals with me or Uncle Sam or any FBI or anybody, because those people wouldn't let me shoot at Butch. They know that I'm on my own – just me, you, and a hole in my shoulder someplace.'

'But,' she says, 'we're not going to stick around. After we get your money—'

'That's a problem too,' I tell her. 'They also know now to alert the people in that bank where I got my stash, you understand, because they know that while I'm here without money it's no good for me. The bank people would naturally have told them whether I was in or not. So they know I haven't got the money and I'm probably going to try and get it. And they're going to be waiting. I can see Butch right now,' I say. 'He's standing on his toes. He's so excited when he smells the kill, because he almost got it. If I try to go back there and take another pop at him they're going to be laying for me. You can bet that Butch ain't going to go running down the street this time. From here on in, until I either get the money or he finds out somebody else gave it to me or something, Butch and his whole mob are going to be parking, and anyone that even looks like me is going to be shot.'

And I'm thinking to myself, I'd still like to whack him out. I'd go out there, go in the back door and hold his mother or his sister and her kid and let him know that if he don't come in the door alone I'll blast them.' Fine. It would work, except I can't do it. I wouldn't want them to

164

do that to me. Bad enough I done these other things. Maybe Butch would do it, but I can't.

'Nancy, you're right,' I tell her. 'We got to try and get some strength back into me here, and one way or the other we got to figure out how we're going to get our money.' And, then I'm starting to think that maybe we should leave without the money and come back some other time.

And she says, 'Well, why don't we go down to Tampa, to my family, maybe they can hide us out there for a while.'

'Do you really think that they don't know you got family in Tampa? They have someone alerted in that area looking for us right now. Do you understand, Nancy, it's you and me against the whole goddamn world now? It's you and me. We got to fight everybody. Don't have any friends, relatives, or nothing anymore, just two souls lost and that's the end of it.'

'Listen,' she tells me, 'let's forget about the bank. You can't go near it right now, people are going to be looking.'

And I'm saying, 'I don't care whether they're looking or not, we need money desperate.'

'But we have enough to get out of here. Let's get out into the country and just play it cool. After a week or so they might let down their guard.'

'Nancy,' I say, 'we don't even have that much. Anyway I love you too much to keep us stashed in these ratholes. I got to get some real money in my hands so we can start a new life.'

This is nothing new with us, you know. We used to talk a lot about taking off. A lot of times in the back of our minds even before I got in trouble, we wished I could dump all of it and just run away, and live out on a farm, you know, just her and I. I was getting fed up with the shit, you know what I mean? And a lot of times, I'm going to tell you the truth, guys do get fed up. You know, the boss'll come down and say, 'I want you to go hit so and so.' And you don't want to do it. The guy is your friend, and you begin thinking that the next time he might tell someone to whack you out. The only trouble was the income was too great to just give it up, and that's the only way I was going to walk away from it. I'd have to go to the Old Man and say, 'I want to get out. Here's all my businesses, my bookmaking operation, and my loan-sharking, the whole works, you people own it all.' This is the only way they were going to let me out.

Anyway, if I ask the Old Man to let me out he's either going to say, 'Yeah, okay,' and mean it or he's going to say, 'Yeah, okay,' and have me killed. One of the two. And most of the time if there's enough money involved and they know that you're not going to come back they'll let you go. They don't give a shit, you know? In fact, some of the time they'd rather see you cut loose because they figure, hey, if you got some kind of thoughts in your mind that you want to quit, maybe you're also thinking of doing something wrong, so they give you a little rope and see how you run. Now, if you go out there and mind your business, no one's going to bother you. It's not like in the movies where you can't retire because you know too much and might blow the whistle. That's not it at all. What they worry about is you trying to get back in. Like all them old-time mobsters staying around Hot Springs and in Saratoga upstate. They sit around and take the baths and talk about the old days and, God knows, as long as they stick to themselves nobody bothers them. But every once in a while, one of them wants to be a drugstore cowboy again and says, 'I'm going to take over,' and goodbye, someone pops him. So if I told the Old Man I was leaving, I had to cut off all relationships. I could never come back and say, 'Listen, I want this business back,' because they won't stand for it. They'd hit you in the head. So, what did I do? I wanted out, but there's nothing I could

166

do about it because the only money I could take is what I've got stashed.

I would have loved to just go away with my *goumara* to a desert island and stay there the rest of my life. But I knew I had a good taste for living. I would never go on an island and live in a shack. I'd want to retire in a mansion with all kinds of servants, private beaches, and all this business. And the only way I could do that was with money, but what the hell's six hundred grand to a wiseguy? You know what I mean? At least two, three million dollars would be a desirable fund to retire with. Because, understand something, I got no skills. Outside of being a wiseguy, I got no skills. So if it comes to pass that I got to go to work because I'm running low on money, what can I do? I mean, can I go and be a brain surgeon? I've opened enough brains in my time. You know, can I become a piano teacher, a scientist? I can't become nothing. So I'm actually thinking of going and just retiring.

The stash won't be enough. But maybe I don't have to live like a king. And right now it seems like a lot and I got to get my hands on it or we're not going much further. Nancy is perfectly right to tell me that it's dangerous as hell to go for the stash and we should wait around until it's cooled down a bit. But I can't wait, I really can't. The longer I hang back, the more reasons she's going to find for not going for the stash. And Butch, he's not really going to take his eyes off it until he knows I'm dead.

# CHAPTER SIX

It takes a couple of hours, but I finally talk Nancy into driving back into Manhattan. I get her to agree that we should make a try at the bank. I'm all bandaged up and my clothes are shabby looking. She's washed them out as much as she can, but what can you do when things got blood all over them and everything? So she stops at a little Army-Navy store and runs in and buys me one of those cheap canvas jackets, to cover myself up so that I won't look so bad. And I try it on and it fits. At least it's clean. I wish we could have bought more clothes, some good ones, but we're really low on money now, only a couple of hundred left, counting what she brought with her.

We get into the Brooklyn-Battery tunnel and come out way downtown and cruise around until we find Broadway and the Irving Trust Company. I get out of the car and I'm walking slow and looking and thinking how Butch might cover the bank. The only way I can figure it is how I'd do it. So I guess he won't have anybody outside, like the news-stand guy at the subway entrance. And I'm not worried about snipers on the buildings around here. You see, it's not like the trial. He don't know when I'm coming to this bank. Could be today, tomorrow, next month. He's got to have people in place at the bank, who are going to be there anyway because they work there. And he has some of his own people who watch them and keep an eye out for me. But he can't have too many wiseguys down here. This is the First Precinct, the one with all the big banks and the gold, and the cops have orders to pick up anyone who might be a thief and escort them uptown and tell them to stay the hell out of this neighborhood. So, that means that Butch has a guy, maybe two, but no more.

So I got to check this place out very careful but casual, and I get to the corner and decide to go to the Broadway entrance, not the one on Wall Street. The Wall Street door is right on the street. The Broadway entrance lets you inside the building, but you got to go through another door to get in the bank, and there's elevators there in front of the bank door, so's you have an excuse to check out the bank without being noticed. I can't remember if I picked this bank because it has two doors, but right now I'm glad I did. So I mosey into the entrance to the building and turn to the elevator and there's some people standing there and I join the crowd and move over to the doors to the bank. It's darker out here than in there and they'll never notice me. The only worry I have is the elevator starter there. Anyway, I make like I'm looking at a piece of paper I got in my hand and I spot a guy inside. I walk a little closer to the door and stay partly hidden, and sure enough there's Charlie the Wiseguy down the end of the counter talking to a tomato, the cashier, which must be the connection. In a way it's good that I find this out because when I come back later, I can try and make it when she's out to lunch. Anyway, I take it all in and I go back to the car and I say, 'Can't get in there, there's somebody that would definitely recognize me.' And I explain it all to Nancy that this broad is talking to my friend Charlie, my ex-friend, and it's obvious that they got the bank staked out. So, I lean back in the seat and I'm wondering what the hell to do. Wait and see who takes the next shift from Charlie and hope it's someone who don't know me by sight? Hang around until he takes a leak and then duck in fast? Try and disguise my face with makeup so even Charlie don't know me? What? I'm sitting stewing all this over and there's a tapping on the car window. It's a cop and he sneaked upon us. I'm trying to smile but my guts are flipping over. I start to open the door and he bends down and yells, 'Move it! You can't park here, folks!' I'm mumbling, Thank you, Thank you, and Nancy starts the car up and we move. I take it as a sign, you know, an omen that, maybe, this is not the right time to go for the stash. 'Maybe we ought to take your advice,' I say to Nancy. 'Get out in the country, give me a little chance to get some of my strength back, too.' And I'm thinking that I know there's at least two at the bank. But how many others? Like, maybe there was another wiseguy off having coffee, or they got him spotted down in the vault. And the cashier. Is she the only one? I doubt it. They got to have at least two or three to make sure. You know, this one gets the curse and don't come in, they got to have others.

So, Nancy starts going uptown on West Street and we get to the Holland Tunnel, which makes me feel a lot safer. We're not out in the open anymore – there's a trailer truck in front of us and there's a trailer behind us and one beside us. We come out onto the New Jersey side and she just starts heading south, figuring that we're going to stash ourselves someplace out in the country. When she gets down off the Jersey Turnpike she's going to get out into that Pennsylvania back country there, couple of hundred miles down the road and stay there for a while until we decide what we're going to do.

We're going down the highway and I tell Nancy, 'Pull over in the next restaurant stop we come to. I'm getting tired and you got to be tired from driving. Let's get some coffee and something to eat. I'm starting to get real hungry.' So we pull into a Howard Johnson's parking lot and there are dozens and dozens of trucks there. We go in. I'm taking a shot to go in there, but I got to move around because I'm getting all cramped up and I just don't feel good. We go into the restaurant and sit amongst some drivers and have some coffee and I can't help hear them talking. They're asking each other, 'Hey, what're you carrying tonight?'

'Well, I got a load of dresses,' one guy says to the other. And, 'I got a load of frozen turkeys for D.C. What you got?'

Then one guy pops up he's hauling a load of RCA televisions, and my ears perk up. I could move them fast if I had them. This might be the out, I'm saying to myself. If I can crown this guy and get his load, I know I can dump it. So I nudge Nancy and I whisper in her ear, 'Listen, just follow me whatever I do. I'm going to try and take this guy. I don't want to really knock his brains in, I just want to get his load and we'll head down the pike.' She looks at me like I'm crazy and I smile, shrug, and make a sign for her to keep quiet. I know she'll follow me and I can explain later.

So Nancy thinks I'm nuts to try a hijacking right here in the open on a public highway. Well, it is a fool's errand, but we need money. I'd really be crazy to try to walk into a store and take pot luck on what's in the register. I mean, the guy behind the counter might have a gun or some alarm might start going off. So the safest score I can think of right now is this guy and his trailer. Sure it's a risk. Even if I robbed a bag of lollipops and resell them it's a risk. So I might as well fence something we can walk away with besides conversation. A load of TV's is almost as good as cash.

About twenty minutes after we come in, some of the truckers finish eating and the guy I'm after heads out with another driver and I follow them but I'm sweating it out because now I got both together and I'm saying to myself, 'Well, geez, maybe these two guys are both on the same rig. I can't handle the two of them. Lucky if I can take one of them in the condition I'm in.'

And then I put my hand in my pocket and I feel that gun down there. Even though it's empty, the guy I'm going to take don't know that. And I follow them out of the restaurant building and one guy splits off and goes to another trailer and the guy I'm following goes to a big General Motors tractor-trailer. I'm walking behind him and I want to throw him off so I make like I'm going to maybe take a leak in the grass over there. He looks around a little and pays no attention and as he turns away I hustle up a little faster. And then the guy turns and asks, 'Can I help you, pal?'

'Yeah, you can help me,' I say and pull out the gun. 'Get your hands up, don't move a muscle, and go around the other side of the tractor.' Now Nancy comes running over. She's got adhesive tape from the bag of medicine she's got to bandage me, and I tell the guy, 'Put your hands behind your back.'

'What do you want from me?' the guy says.

'Are you crazy?' I yell a little, 'Put your hands behind your back and don't give me no argument or I'll split your head open.'

'I don't want no trouble,' he says. 'Take anything you want.'

'I'm going to take it all, never mind anything I want. Now, if you want to live to see your family or whatever you got at home, be a nice guy and shut your mouth.' And he puts his hands behind him and Nancy wraps him real tight with tape and puts some over his mouth. There's no sense in closing his eyes because he's already seen me. And I tell the guy, 'Jump up in the cab there and back in the sleeper.' Then I wrap his feet with tape a couple of times. And I get behind the wheel and crank down the window and tell Nancy, 'Okay, now you get in the car and follow me.'

Suddenly, I start to feel pretty good. I know the feeling. It comes when you just made a score. It's the greatest feeling in the world. Here I am taking wild chances that I might get picked up and thrown in the can and I don't care. Since I left Washington three days ago – it seems like three weeks – I already broke parole, did assault and battery, robbery (armed and unarmed), illegal possession, attempted murder, and now hijacking and interstate transportation of stolen goods. The only things I left out is dope and counterfeiting. I even spit on the sidewalk and double-parked.

Nancy's following me down the road, and I got the guy stashed in the back so I know nobody's got a ticket out on us yet.

Now I'm rolling down the highway and I'm thinking about getting to a phone and calling this fence I know. I'm asking myself, 'Is it smart to call him in advance?' Well, its the only way, because I might get all the way down to Richmond and find out this guy ain't even around anymore. What I'll do is wait till I get a little further south so that if he alerts anyone back in New York he couldn't alert them fast enough to hurt me. And I'm planning on him being discreet, the way I always knew him. And when he hears that he can buy a trailerload of RCA televisions dirt cheap he's not going to call the mob until I leave, so? He's going to try and steal them. The guy is Abbie the Jew, and I've sold him many a load of cigarettes and liquor. There's one thing I got to say about these fences – whenever you call them, no matter what hour of the day or night, it's 'How much is the load?' and 'It's not worth that much' and 'I wanna give you this much.' Abbie is always business and he always kept his word financially. No problems with the money. Buys anything. No questions asked. Dead solid with the mob because he always keeps his mouth shut.

I climb down out of the cab and get in a roadside phone booth and close my eyes trying to remember the creep's number. I been thinking on it for the last twenty miles and suddenly it comes to me and I dial. No one ever marks them things down, but you remember. Because if you get caught with them, numbers like that, you're in trouble with the cops. I mean, you could be what the police thought was a nobody. And then, all of a sudden, they pick you up for a stupid charge and they find all these numbers, and they're going to start really leaning on you, because they know who the fences are, see?

The phone's ringing and, click, it's picked up, 'Yeah?'

'Abbie, this is a friend of yours. Don't ask no questions because your phone might be tapped, you know.' I'm trying to throw him off guard. 'I got a package for you here, a very, very expensive package, something that I know you'll be wanting. Can you use it?'

'Well, you're not telling me what it is . . .'

'I can't tell you what it is right now, but I'm sure you'll be able to do what you want with it.'

'Okay, here's another number. Call me back.' So I hang up and I call him back on the other number, a pay phone that he has in his building there.

'What is it you got?' says Abbie.

'I got a load of televisions for you, RCA.'

'Oh, Jesus, I don't know if I can use the whole load.'

'Look, you bastard, don't try to be a wise ass, you know you want the whole load. You're going to look to steal it from me? I'm going to let you steal it from me. I want fifteen percent of whatever the load is worth. Fifteen percent ain't a lot of money; you get a third at least. I only want fifteen percent and I need it fast.'

'Well, okay . . .'

'I don't want no advertising on this. Keep your mouth shut and I'll keep mine shut, you get your money and you don't have to split it with nobody.' I say that because one time Abbie had to kick in a piece of everything he earned to the mob because the mob was the only ones doing business with him. And now I'm telling him he's going to buy it for nothing and he don't have to kick into nobody. And when I hang up I'm thinking to myself the son-of-a-bitch's eyes must be opening up.

'Can you trust him?' Nancy's saying.

'No, I can't trust him, I can't trust nobody in this world but you,' I say. 'But I have to trust him because we can't go any further. The only thing I can trust in is this man's a greedy bastard, always has been, and that's why I laid the candy on him. Fifteen percent, that's unheard of. He'd give fifteen percent just to look at it, never mind own it, and not only that, he knows that he don't have to tell anybody how much he got. He can turn around and say, "Johnny Forza brought me a dozen televisions," because he knows I'm going to be dead once they catch up with me.'

'Well, I don't know,' Nancy says. 'Maybe it's a stupid move and maybe we can do without it, John. We got all the time in the world. Why take foolish chances?'

And I say, 'Nancy, we don't have no time. Don't you understand that? We're almost out of money. And I got to get some rest. At least let's get our hands on some real money and we'll hole up someplace for a week or two, a month maybe. We'll just take it easy, I'll relax, and pretty soon I'll feel a hundred percent better and then we'll . . .'

'Well, all right, if you say so. What do you want me to do?'

'You just keep following me, that's all,' I tell her. And now we head down Route Ninety-Five around Washington and into Virginia.

We get to Richmond early evening and I remember where Abbie's place is, a warehouse in an old factory district. I go down there, park the truck on a side street nearby, and get in the car with Nancy, and we start going back and forth all over the neighborhood to see if anything looks suspicious. I'm paranoid. If a sparrow flies by I think it's a hawk. And the area is very, very quiet. It's after business hours and there's nobody on the streets and it seems pretty safe to me. So we pull up to Abbie's in the car. In the meantime the trailer's still parked a couple of blocks away with the guy stashed in the back. I know I can't leave him there too long. Some cop might come by and try to give me a ticket, you know, and take a look in the cab and find him. So, I tell Nancy to let me out in front of Abbie's house and go back and keep an eye on the trailer from a distance.

I knock on the door. This little bald-headed bastard comes to the door. 'Oh ! It's you !' He makes like I'm a big surprise.

'Who the hell was you expecting, Santa Claus?' And I say, 'Listen, I got no time to fool around. I got a load of televisions and the seal hasn't even been broken. You and I both know what wholesale prices are on these things. We agreed to fifteen percent. No argument and nothing.'

'So?'

'So, where do you want me to put the load?'

'Back it in around to the back side of the warehouse,' he says. I start to turn away and then I come back to him, take out my gun and put it right to his head. I say, 'Listen,' and I pull the goddam hammer back, 'I'm going to spatter you all over the building if you so much as go near a a telephone or put the finger on me. You're buying this load for fifteen percent, you can steal it from me, I'm not interested. I know ten minutes after I leave you're going to be on the phone with New York. Good luck to you. I don't even care. All I want is you buy the stuff from me now and then do what you want.' So I walk a couple of blocks back to the truck. I'm on the corner and Nancy gives me the okay that no one's been near it. I get in and check on the guy. He's awake and he's moving from side to side and trying to get loose, pleading with me with his eyes. I say, 'Sorry, pal. I know the trouble you got because I got the same thing.' So we're in gear now and I'm pulling out very slowly and cautiously. I guess I want to make sure that I haven't been spotted, not that I could do much if I have been.

Down a couple of blocks I come to the warehouse. I back the trailer in there and Abbie has three black guys on the platform to help me unload the thing with a forklift. These TVs are on pallets and we take a fast look at what's there. It takes about three hours sweating it out there – the longest three hours of my life. Nancy pulls in the back, and stays in the car with the motor running just in the event we got to get out of there fast.

All the TVs are supposed to come to about $28,000. Now, Abbie knows I'm in trouble, and he tries to beat me out of a little money, naturally. He offers me $15,000, and I surprise him, I say 'Okay, a deal. Fifteen in tens, twenties, nothing bigger than a fifty.' And I can see his face fall a little. The fuck is sorry he didn't knock me down to twelve. So Abbie goes over to his safe, a double-door jobs that stands four feet high and looks like it's been through the Civil War. And he spins with the dial and opens it and pulls out a tin box and counts me out fifteen in tens, twenties and fifties, puts a rubber band around the pile, and stuffs it in a paper bag. 'The bag is on the house,' he says. A joker. And I get up, feeling very tall and strong, and slap Abbie on the back.

Fifteen thousand. Fantastic! In a pile it stands maybe two inches high. Packed this way it takes up the same room as six packs of cigarettes. It'll buy us a car and six months in the sun somewhere. Or, and I'm grinning at the memory, I could blow it at the track in an hour, at Vegas in fifteen minutes, over the phone in thirty seconds. And Abbie's saying, 'You got to get this trailer outa here.' He's right. Number one, I got to wipe it down because this is one rap I can't take, you know, I mean I'm gone with the wind anyway, but this is grand larceny and they could tie me to it easy. Also, I got to get this guy sprung loose that's in back of me here, you know? So I pull it out and get back on the highway, drive down to the next rest stop, and pull in where all the other trucks are. I tell the guy, 'Don't worry, pal, I'm going to go and call the police and tell them where you are, because I don't want to see you hurt anymore.'

I don't know what Abbie is doing, naturally, but I can guess. I can count on the bastard to be on the phone with New York five minutes after I'm out the door.

'I didn't want to buy it, Butch, I didn't wanna buy it,' I can just imagine him saying. 'He forced me at gunpoint. You can ask the guys that work here, he come in at gunpoint with this load. I didn't know he was coming, he never called me. He just walked in on me. As soon's I got a chance to get to the phone I called you.' And Butch is yelling at him, calling him a fucking Jew bastard. I can almost hear the both of them.

So, I wipe down the trailer and dump it in the parking lot, just walk away from it, go to the phone and dial the local police department. I tell them, 'Check a GM trailer at the such-and-such rest stop,' and I hang up. Then I get in the car with Nancy and off we go down the highway. I tell her to try and find someplace where we can lay our heads down for a few hours. She don't want to stay at any place right on the beaten path, she wants to get off. I lay my head back on the seat and I'm trying to relax a little bit, trying to forget about the pain. She reaches over and pats my hand and so forth. I really feel a little bit secure now, and I'm half-asleep.

We get off the highway and she finds a nice-looking place but not a chain joint, you know, a mongrel joint. She goes in and registers and comes out with the key, and says, 'Come on, honey, I'm going to get you to bed. You really need it.' And we walk in the room and immediately I go and lay down on the bed. And Nancy lies beside me and massages my neck and head and calls me her big, tough creampuff and we kiss and we make love and for a while I don't even notice the pain in my shoulder. I must have fallen asleep because when I wake up she's sitting in a chair looking at me and smoking a cigarette. And I can tell she's feeling nervous. And she looks like she's been crying and she tells me she talked to her mother in Florida and she asks me flat out, 'What do we do now? I mean can we go on like this forever?'

I'm more than a little pissed at her for calling Florida because I already told her the mob's got people looking for me in Tampa. They might even have her mother's phone watched, if not tapped. You know, they can watch a phone by having someone in the telephone office there note down when a toll call comes in for that number and they can get the calling number, which is a help even without the message. Who else but Nancy would call Nancy's mother long distance? I got to chew her out about that. But I got another beef to raise first. I think her mother's been at her again about why she goes with me. So I say, 'You know I'm a thief. I grew up in a neighborhood of thiefs. You were either a good thief or a bad thief. A bad thief starved. A good thief made good. But my family had it good. I'm a thief because I want to be a thief. I wasn't forced into it.'

And she smiles at me and says, 'Johnny, it's not that. I don't care what you do. I never did. I love you. It's just that I hate living like this never knowing . . .' I hold up my hand and stop her.

'What's the sense you asking me what are we going to do? I haven't the slightest idea. I don't want to yell at you. I don't want to take out my frustrations. I'm glad you're here because I love you so much. But you got to stop aggravating me by asking me what we're going to do. We're going to do whatever we can do. Because, let me tell you something, Nancy, right now if we argue amongst ourselves and we split up it gives Butch that much more chance to kill us both, because you're dead now. You know too much. You think he would let you live?'

'I know that,' she says, 'and I don't care. I don't want to fight with you, honey. But I also don't want to run the rest of my life like a bum and sleep in dirty old motels. You must have some kind of a plan.'

'Nancy, all I want to do is to get enough money put together so we can maybe get out of the country. Go to Mexico, from there to South America, from there, maybe to Europe. But we can't do nothing without money. It's a hell of a risk for you and for me too. But we got to take it, no other way out.'

'My mother tells me that one of my friends has been around,' she said.

'You're not stupid!' I tell her. 'You know who that is. It's one of the boys checking out to see if you been in the area, if your mother's heard from you. That means we can't go anywhere near her, not even you alone. Right now they know that you're with me. And if you went there alone, they'd grab you, honey; you don't understand but they would grab you.'

You see, the trouble is, Nancy don't know the mob first-hand and like I do. She knows more about it than my wife, but I still never told her the hard parts, the things that happen to guys. So I say, 'They would grab you and torture you. I mean, that bit about someone going down there – you're not stupid enough to fall for that, that it was really some friend of yours? It was one of the boys that Butch sent down there, "Take a check around, check the neighborhood, see if they seen anyone answering Nancy's description. Go knock on the door and say, 'Gee, I'm a friend of Nancy's just traveling through, you know. Would you know if she's coming down? I checked her house in New York and she's not there.' " '

I say to Nancy, 'They got someone laying everywhere for us. But if we stick together, we got a good chance to get away from all this.' I'm saying this to her, but in the back of my mind, I'm saying, 'We ain't got a chance. We ain't got a yam's chance in the Ku Klux Klan. There's only one thing to do and that's try and get the money. Right now, as bad as I got it in for Butch, I can't even consider going after him again. Now that I'm feeling a little better, my head is screwed on a little tighter and I think that Nancy's right – to try to get at this guy again is foolhardy. He's got an army behind him. I took one Pearl Harbor at him and that was it. I missed. I might have blown the whole situation. I might have blown the bank, too.

I got one hope left, that my dealing with Abbie the Jew works out the way I planned. I hope I'm right about Abbie. I hope that he called Butch and told him I was down there and that he gave me money, a fair amount of money . . . I got to put myself in Butch's shoes : would I think that this guy Johnny went south? After that close call in New York – the shooting, the cops up in arms for me, my parole officer looking for me, maybe the marshals looking – I would have to say Butch has got to believe that I got a few grand in my pocket and I got Nancy with me and I'm going to head south. Butch knows that Nancy's family lives down in Tampa, and he don't think we're dumb enough to go to their house, but he knows how much we like to take the sun. You know, Nancy and me used to cut out for the beach any time we could get away with it. Didn't matter where as long as it wasn't cloudy – Acapulco, Jamaica, Nassau, Portugal, Hawaii. We even went to Greece one time. We'd go, spend a few days getting a tan, and then dress in white and knock 'em dead on the dance floor. You think Nancy is a dish, you ought to see her in a white dress after a week in the sun. Wow!

There's only one problem. I'm thinking, this may be too easy. I don't know what Abbie told Butch, but if he told him the whole bit, then Butch is going to wonder why I practically told Abbie to spill to him. Why would he think I'd do that? The only reason I could have is that I want Butch to know I made a score. And I want him to know so's he thinks I got the money to travel, and this is going to make Butch think I'm trying to pull a fast one and come right back to town instead of heading south.

But wait a minute. If Butch figures I think he's looking for me to head for the sun, then he's going to guess I think he *expects* me to try for the stash instead. Understand? He's left in the middle – am I dumb or brighteyes? And he's got one more piece; he knows I'm hurt and need a place to lie down. So, take it all – he's going to think I'd hide out, but maybe north and not south. He checks Saranac Lake, the resorts, Montreal – and he keeps a little peek on the stash. And I think I can take care of a little peek.

So I say, 'Nancy, come on, let's go, we'll buy a car, and head back for the stash.' And I'm planning the whole thing in my head like it was some kind of score that I was going after and, of course, it *is* a score. The difference is that it's mine. We're going to buy a car for cash down here in a phony name, get what clothes we need, and pick up some kind of disguise for me – maybe a man's wig or a beard. They sell them now in barber shops. And we'll put ourselves together and we'll head back. It's the weekend now, and we'll want to get there Monday morning bright and early. We're going to walk in and see if that girl is on a coffee break or whatever – you know, the girl who was talking to Charlie the Wiseguy. And I'll lay for her and go in when she's away from her desk.

So, we go to a car dealer in Charlottesville, who's got a lot full of used cars. And I find a black Ford Galaxie, good shape but not flashy, and I ask how much he wants for it.

'Got a special on it today, eight ninety-five.' A big smile.

I tell the guy, 'Okay, this car here's okay, can you take anything off for cash?' I got to at least look like I'm trying to get the guy down or he's going to remember me as the biggest jerk he seen in years.

'No, I can't,' he says. 'This is the price and that's it. Car's a real bargain, low mileage and all.'

'Okay,' I say, 'I need the car bad. Can you get plates for it immediately because I got a trip to go on?'

'Yeah, what's the name?' And I give him James Marco. With cash in the Virginia area, even in the Carolinas, you can buy a car under any name you want. And I say, 'Here's a fifty dollar bill for you for getting it done fast for me. And, by the way, I'm infected, I don't wanna say where, it's a personal problem, you know, could you get me some pills?'

'Oh, I don't fool around with that,' he says, 'I'm no pusher or anything.'

'I don't mean pusher, I mean even a doctor I could go to give me a prescription for pain.'

Then he says, 'I know a guy that might look the other way and give you a prescription.'

'Okay, you take care of it for me and there's a few bucks in it for you.' He gets me the medicine and I duke him a few. We hang around there an hour or so while he has a runner go for the plates and puts some insurance on it and a couple hours later we're on our way with pills and everything. We cleaned out Nancy's car and we left it. No sense in worrying about it; we're never going to have the chance to collect insurance or anything else. Just park it there on the side of the road and head back up north. We take our own good time, figuring we'll drive until we get tired.

Right now, Nancy's driving and I'm going through the whole bank scene in my head, walking through the door and up to the old guy who checks you in to go down to the safe-deposit area. And in my head I walk down the stairs and hand the girl my key and she pushes the book over to me to sign and it's perfect. And I'm beginning to smile at what it'll feel like to get my hands on that money – all those packages of hundred-dollar bills – and I turn to Nancy and I see she's real ticked off. She's not saying nothing, hasn't said a word in twenty miles, and she's got a funny blank look on her face. That's what she's like when she's mad. So, I put my hand on her knee and, 'Okay, what's the matter, Nance?'

She takes a deep breath and lets it out. 'Oh, Johnny.' She looks over at me. 'You're not strong enough for this thing we're on our way to do. We don't have to do it now. With the money we just picked up we can live for six months down south and Butch'll get tired of looking and we can go back nice and quiet and get it and not take big chances.'

I smooth her hair with my hand and say, 'First, we can't live for six months on no fifteen grand. We can keep from starving but it's not going to be living. It's going to be one crummy motel after another. It's not going to be safe and it's not going to be relaxing. It's not going to be anything but a royal pain in the ass . . .' I'm yelling a little bit and she's started to smile. Nancy always did like my temper as long as it didn't get too bad. 'Look,' I say, 'the safest thing I can do is go for the stash right now. Butch is going to figure that I'll lay low after making that score and he'll be looking for us in all the places out of New York that we might head for.' Naturally, I don't tell her that Butch might figure that I'd do just what I'm doing and that, no matter what, he's not going to leave the bank unguarded. But why should I worry her? No point to it. If I tell her the truth we never go back for the stash.

We're coming into the city now and I'm nervous as hell. We take the same route as before – the Holland

Tunnel downtown. It's closer to the bank than the other ones and you get more trucks than cars through it. We both changed our appearances overnight. I've got myself all rigged up like an actor – long-haired wig to make me look a little hippieish, fake beard and fake mustache and a pair of shades. And Nancy has had her hair cut – one of those shingled jobs – and dyed sort of brownish, nothing you'd notice. Like I said, it's much easier for a woman to change her appearance: they do it every day, you know. And with Nancy a lot of it was just toning herself down. Instead of putting a little extra swing into her rear end when she's walking, she slows down and watches herself. Instead of taking a deep breath when people are looking at her to show her chest, she breathes normally. Anyway, we're both dressed in blue-jean outfits she's picked out and wearing sneakers. And here it is about ten o'clock in the morning and we pull up to the bank and I check the window and, sure enough, the broad's still in there, the one on the end, so I decide to wait it out for a while. The best move is when she goes out – she's got to go out some time – so I'm standing there saying to myself, 'Well, did I get spotted coming into New York? Are they laying for me again?' Because if I was in Butch's shoes and Johnny Forza got spotted in this city, the first thing I'd have on mind is he's going for the stash. Otherwise, he would have no reason to come back here, other than to kill me. So I'd have to cover the bank.

Now, I know that in this outfit I'm wearing I'm not going to fool anyone that really knows me, but Butch can't have Charlie the Wiseguy in the bank every day, can he? Maybe he can. I'm standing outside there waiting, smoking a cigarette, and I'm maybe thirty feet down on the sidewalk from the Wall Street entrance of the bank. And I'm thinking about how easy it is to get money out of banks and how easy it would be to rip this one off if Butch didn't have it covered. I don't mean stick up the joint or blow the vault, I mean a scam. People who work in banks are scared, and if you growl at them a little bit and you act indignant they want to give you the money and get you out of the place, you know. Like when I was with Tony L. doing Wall Street and cashing phony checks and so forth, he'd go in and always use names like Wolfgang Chisholm, names like that, and the girl would say, 'What's your name, sir?'

'Wolfgang Chisholm – what are you laughing at? Are you making fun of my name?' He'd be dressed up in spats with a little derby on, and he'd say, 'Well, let's see what your manager thinks.'

'Wait a minute, sir. I didn't mean that.' And she couldn't get us the money fast enough. Take all that and get the hell out of here. She didn't want to get in trouble with her manager and out we'd go with the money. Wall Street, for chrissake. And we cashed checks for $6,800, $7,800, right in the bank without having an account there. We had a way we used to get a copy of the okay of the manager of the bank on a small check and trace it onto a larger one. I would walk from the teller's window to the manager and while I was there, I'd just have conversation, give him something to write something down, then I'd head back and Tony would hit the teller with the check with the okay on the back, you see. It was original, a bona fide okay, no forgery, a trace job right over his signature. You always pick a young girl cause they're scared of losing their job. You pick a seasoned old pro, she don't want to know nothing and you get nothing from her.

I'm watching for the cashier and after about fifteen or twenty minutes she's gone. Whether she's going to a coffee break or to the ladies' room, I don't know. I mean she goes out from around the counter, heads where it says 'Bank Employees Only,' and meantime, I'm fingering that key and my identification as John Forza. So, I go in fast and walk back to where they have this old-timer back there that has record books you have to sign to get into the safety-deposit vault. You got to sign upstairs to get downstairs. And I show my key and the old man's taking his sweet time checking the register numbers and so forth, and I'm looking around nonchalantly. There's a couple of guards there, both retired policemen or whatever, and they're about the age limit, not young fellows. They got their guns on but they're just wandering around; they don't pay no attention to nobody, because that's the way banks are.

'Right down here, Mister Forza,' and I look at him close and he's not even paying a bit of attention to me, like Mister Forza don't mean nothing to him at all, this old-timer that's at the desk, and I walk downstairs and I'm saying to myself, 'Look back over your shoulder to see if this guy's picking up a phone or anything,' and he does pick up a phone. I don't know where he's calling, he could be calling downstairs to the vault and saying 'Mister Forza's coming down there, give him—' but you don't know. Right off the bat, my legs start shaking again. So now I quicken my step a bit more, I mean not too fast cause I don't want to be obvious, but a little bit more, you know, because I want to get in and get out of there.

I get to the bottom of the stairs and there's a woman behind the iron gate, and she asks, 'Mister Forza?' and I show my key again and so forth and she says, 'Thank you,' and hits the buzzer and I'm in the vault. She leads me inside and she puts a key in box 281. I put my key in the same box and she turns them both, pulls the box out and hands it to me. And I take the box and walk out of the vault and over to a little booth where I can open up my box. I open it up – and breathe with relief that it's still there : packages of hundred dollar bills, ten thousand to a package. More than half a million bucks.

I start putting the money into a briefcase I brought

with me: fifty-eight packages of money and I still got room to spare. I fit a million in one so easily, many a time. And I got another gun in there, by the way, and some jewelry in a little bag, hot diamonds and stuff, mostly unset. And I'm thinking to myself, 'Thank God I had the brains to stash these diamonds, because even if you went to Russia, diamonds are good. American money might not be good over there, but them diamonds are good everywhere.' And I got about eighty, ninety thousand dollars' worth of diamonds – no serial numbers on diamonds – in a little bag. You could walk anywhere with it; you could walk through customs and put it in your mouth and no one's going to be the wiser. And even if they were found, the only thing they can ask you to do is pay duty on them, you see?

So I stash everything in my briefcase and I want to get out real fast and I'm walking to the iron gate and the woman says, 'Mister Forza? Mister Forza?' And I'm thinking, what the hell is the matter now? I turn around. 'You forgot to put the box back in and take your key,' she smiles at me.

Little things like this are shaking me up tremendously, you know. I mean other times I would never forget a stupid thing like this. And I walk back and get the box and I apologize. So I put the box back in there and we lock it up together and she gives me back my key and I sign out because you have to sign out like you sign in. And I'm walking up the stairs and the sweat is starting to pour off me. Looks like I got a hundred miles to walk to get outside. I'm saying to myself, 'Honey, I'm on the way. Now I got this damn stash, now we got one leg up on it, we can get the hell out of the country.' I keep thinking, 'Let me think of only good things, because if I start thinking of the bad things I might not make it up the stairs.'

Thinking of good things is easy because down in the little room where I just got my box they have travel posters all over the wall, you know? Couple drinking at a table in front of a white stone house and blue sky all around. Sunshine everywhere. A beautiful girl on a sailboat. I'm coming up the stairs thinking how beautiful it's going to be to lay down in South America on the beach some place with my baby and be able to take a nice trip to Europe and how beautiful life can be now that we're escaping from all these lice. I get up near the top of the stairs, and I got this bag in my hand like it's my life, and it really is. My life depends on what's in this bag. My life and Nancy's. That's about all I can think about, her life and mine, because nobody else gives a shit about me.

So I get up where my head is starting to see the banking floor and that girl cashier is back.

The old guy is still sitting at the desk and he glances over and asks, 'All finished, Mister Forza?'

'Yeah, everything is fine. Thank you.' And I'm walking nice and slow, like I have no care in the world. I don't want to show anybody that I'm in a hurry to get out, attract attention. I'm thinking that I got it, I got it in my hand. Now I'm down at one end of the lobby and I'm just starting to head towards the main door and I see two guys coming in. They don't really recognize me and I don't recognize them but I know there's something about these two guys. Maybe the way they walk, maybe the way they ... Maybe it's just my animal instinct that tells me these two guys are here to give me a headache. I can see by looking at them; they stick out like a sore thumb, with silk mohair suits in the middle of the daytime. Wiseguys are the only people that do them things. Businessmen wear gray flannel in this area, you know, gray tweeds and things like that. Here they come with these beautiful three-hundred-dollar suits on. They got to be wiseguys. They seem very, very curious, looking around like this. One of them just looked me over very carefully. Did he make me? If he did, is he going to be foolish enough to try and do something here?

And the guy's looking at me and all of a sudden turns around and looks at his friend that he's with and he says something to him, and I'm too far away to make it out. The bastard, he did make me, he's probably saying, 'Shall we knock him dead here or shall we follow him or what?'

What the hell am I going to do now? Should I stop for a minute and see if they come over? Maybe they're going to try and stick a piece in my ribs and walk me out of here. The bastards are coming towards me. What am I going to do?

I look at two bank guards and they're just looking out the window. They don't know what the hell's going on. What am I going to do?

I know I got one thing to do : I gotta take a shot at it. I'm at the end of the lobby of the bank, about fifty feet from them, and I decide to slow down now and get behind one of these marble columns and see if they're actually going to come towards me. If they did spot me and if it is people that are looking for me, they're going to head towards me. Sure enough, they're coming this way. I've been made for sure. I glance over at the cashier and she's on the phone. Is she calling for more help? I don't care; I'm sure she's one of them. I look at the old man, and he's on the phone too. Could they both be on the payroll? Butch's payroll? I say, yeah, the whole bank could be as far as I'm concerned.

Here I'm going to get it, that's the way I feel. And I'm saying, 'Nancy,' to myself, 'Nancy,' and people are standing in line cashing checks and depositing money. There might be seventy-five or a hundred wandering around in this bank and nobody's paying a bit of attention to me. These guys could come up and stick a piece in my ribs and get me out of there with no one noticing a thing. I think about opening up the briefcase. I got a loaded revolver in that bag, but I better not do that because then I'll alert everybody.

Like I said, the only thing I can do is take a chance, so all of a sudden I yell, 'Help! It's a robbery! They're robbing the bank!' And I'm pointing to them. 'That man's got a gun! Help! Police!' And as I'm yelling, one of them damn fools pulls out his piece in the excitement and now the guards are looking and they take their guns out and as they do the wiseguy takes a shot and he wings one of the guards and the other guy pulls his piece and now there a hundred people screaming and running around and I decide that it's time I make a quick evacuation. So I walk out nice and quiet to the side door, the one that leads to Broadway. And behind me there's more shots and in the car outside Nancy's in a panic because she can hear the shots and she don't know what's happening.

I'm walking at a quick pace now. I'm not running. I don't want to attract attention. Open the door, throw myself in the back seat, stash and all, and tell Nancy, 'Don't go fast, nice and slow, pull away from the curb so no one will notice us.' And that's what she does and we get out into traffic and I can hear sirens behind us. The bank-robbery alarm has gone off. Now if Butch was there he wouldn't of went for what I pulled. He would of had men posted outside the bank. These guys walked right in, they didn't spot Nancy, they don't know the new car, they're looking for a different car. So we just drive away quietly and think about nice things for a change.

# CHAPTER SEVEN

My first thought after getting away from the bank is to go to a motel and hole up there until dark. We're going down lower Broadway to Bowling Green and Nancy takes a right over to West Street and another right, and we're almost to the Brooklyn-Battery Tunnel when I nudge her and say, 'Keep on going north.' And she does and after a few blocks I lean over and tell her, 'You know, right now Butch don't know what happened at the bank, but he's going to know in ten, fifteen minutes. So we're in the clear. Keep going. By tonight he has the city sealed tight.'

At Twenty-Second Street she turns into Eleventh Avenue, where there's mostly truck traffic, but I'm very much aware that any car on its way downtown may be Butch's. I lay down on the back seat so I'm not easy to see. I take off the hippie wig and shove it under the front seat. And I got the briefcase on my lap. After a while, I can't resist. I open it just to see if it's all still there. And I reach in and pull out a package – ten thousand in hundred-dollar bills. It's not as thick as my pinkie and it fits into my coat like a wallet.

We're going to go up the New York Thruway into Pennsylvania and try to make it down through the Southwest and over the border into Mexico. But I've planned to head for Mexico so long that Butch probably knows about it like he knew where the stash was. You see, I have a connection at the American Embassy down there and I can give the guys a few big ones and get new U.S. passports in any names I want – not fake or altered ones but real passports. So now I'm thinking maybe we're not going to go that way at all, at least not now. We're going to go north to Canada, just where he wouldn't expect us to head because of all the mob guys in Montreal and Buffalo and along the border, guys that been there since Prohibition and that made their first big dough running booze into the U.S.

So I got to make Butch think for a while anyway that we've gone to Mexico, and the way to do that is to buy tickets and then get a few pieces of luggage, fill them with newspapers and phone books, go to the airport, check the bags in, and then just not get on the plane. So the bags go to Mexico and Butch's people will see them go through the baggage area and think we missed that flight but maybe we'll be on the next one. I'm beginning to like the idea when suddenly I realize that we need tourist cards to buy the tickets and Nancy don't have no fake ID, so we have to get her ticket in her real name. Shit! Butch would never believe that we'd use our own names, so it's not even worth the trouble : he'd ignore the whole bit. And I'm saying to myself, 'It won't keep him off our back. He's not going to know for sure where we went, but he'll check Mexico first thing, and any trail that leads down there is going to make him suspicious.'

The road's getting bumpy so I sit up. We're going up the West Side Highway and as usual it's a mess − full of holes, chunks of concrete, pieces of rubber from tires laying here and there. We're in the center lane and Nancy's only doing forty-five and my teeth are rattling. But we're getting out of town fast. There's hardly any traffic at this hour going north; they're all bumper-to-bumper coming in. And we go under the George Washington Bridge and up the hill nice and easy, and here's one of them crazies. We're coming up to a toll booth and the sign says 'Exact Change Lanes Ahead,' and Nancy's slowing down to forty, when here comes this character tearing around us in a station wagon. Jesus, he's got to cut us off and get in there to throw his quarters in. He's in such a hurry he can't stand it. I'd like to shoot out one of his rear tires and see what the hell he'd do, the son-of-a-bitch. Anyway, we go over the bridge and we're out of Manhattan and in Riverdale – still a part of the city with all these big apartments, but very suburby looking with lots of trees and winding side streets. A little farther on and we're out of the city and into real country.

We've got a pocketful of money and I'm feeling much better in my shoulder and we're in a new car that no one's supposed to know about and we're feeling a little bit relaxed. I'm just laying my head back here and I'm looking at this beautiful broad and saying to myself, 'I finally got it made, after all the years that I had to hide with this tomato and hide from this guy and hide from this guy and hide from that guy, from my wife, and now I'm on the run and I think we got it licked.' And I lean over and I look at her and I'm crazy about her and I think I got the world by the tail.

So we stop for gas at a little station with a slate roof and I decide I want to take a turn at driving, I want to see her face when I talk to her. And I tell her my plan to go to Canada because Butch will be watching for us in Mexico and I say, 'We're going up to Montreal or over there to Buffalo and I kind of think we could lose ourselves in an area like Montreal where I'm not too well known.' So we're driving along and we're on the Taconic Parkway, which is very scenic, very, very twisty but beautiful road no matter what time of year it is. If it's the fall the color is beautiful, if it's the summer the green is beautiful, and in the winter the snow is fantastic. It's just a great ride, with high hills on each side of the road, trees, big rocks. The whole damn state is rock and they use a lot of it to make the walls of those lockups they got there, upstate.

Nancy's checking the road map and then she turns to

me and says, 'Well, you know, we never really had any time to ourselves alone.'

'What are you talking about?' I say. 'We been together for nearly a week.'

'Aw, honey,' she says, cuddling up to me, 'I mean, like we was married, you know. Buffalo is right across from Niagara Falls.'

'You want a honeymoon!' I'm laughing and at the same time liking the idea, so I say, 'Okay, baby, you want a honeymoon, you got a honeymoon. Niagara Falls, here we come!' And I'm figuring what the hell difference does it make? We got to cross someplace and Niagara Falls is going to be crowded with tourists in weather like this, so maybe it's even safer than Montreal or crossing at Detroit.

We're driving along and we see a sign that says 'Somebody's Lookout' and we stop at a place high up where you drive your car off the road. There's a little parking area and a stone wall and you can look down in the valley. Anyway, there's a couple other cars around and it's the kind of thing that I normally wouldn't do. It's the kind of thing, you know, that only suckers do, stand around with their cameras and their binoculars and so on, but I'm feeling like that; I'm feeling – ah, the hell with it – in fact the more I act like a sucker maybe the better it is. And we're standing there holding each other and looking down and you can't see anything but trees and a little river, no houses or towns.

A guy behind me says, 'Excuse me, sir!' I whirl around quick – my gun is back in the car – and then I see this apple standing five feet away with a woman next to him and he holds out a camera. 'Would you take our picture?' he says, and I breathe out with relief and take the camera and hold it up and they stand together and I can see them in the little window, and I say, 'Smile.' I push the button and we do it again a few more times, different poses. And when I'm through he thanks me and Nancy says, 'That was real nice of you, honey.' And I say, 'Look, I never said I didn't like being nice to people.' But I'm thinking, that's bullshit. I did it because the guy would have remembered me if I told him to go fuck off. It was okay acting like that, but I like respect, not 'Thank you because you're such a nice guy.'

We're beginning to act too casual, I'm thinking now, and that worries me a little bit, you know. There's five thousand animals looking for me and every crooked cop in the country has his eye out. To get a speeding ticket in this area could mean the end. A cop might recognize me. And each toll booth we have to pass is a trap, if someone makes me. They could say, 'Hey, Johnny Forza just went through here, he's heading up towards Buffalo,' and the next thing bang, someone lands one on me at the next toll booth. Just because you're stopped by the toll takers for only half a minute don't mean they don't get a good look at you.

We're getting hungry, so I take the next turnoff and we go a mile or two on blacktop and come to a little town full of old houses and winding streets. When you get off a parkway you see another side of life, something like you see from a train window at night. You pass through little towns and you see the little no-name gas stations and the little diners and the grocery stores that have about six cans of something on the shelf, and the road is two lanes wide and your right wheels are almost in somebody's front yard and there are cars parked in drives, kids playing on the lawn, swings, front doors open with a screen door on, and the whole thing is very free and easy. And nobody seems suspicious of anybody else and you know that every door in this town is left unlocked and they all know each other by their first name. It's a slow kind of life, different from Manhattan and the Italian neighborhoods. The Italians who live out here aren't like those in New York. They act like apples. It's only when you get to places like Utica, Troy, Syracuse, Albany, that you get into neighborhoods like Mulberry Street.

And I'm saying to myself, 'Why the hell did I live in Brooklyn all these years when I could have lived out here with all the money I made?' I see people taking kids to school or something and it's nice and comfortable and we stop at a gas station and I see everybody so relaxed instead of grabbing at each other's throats, and it's just a relaxful feeling. There's a gas station that looks like a farmhouse, like it ought to have animals around it, and suddenly the road is enclosed by trees and it's almost like we're way out in the woods and far away from New York City.

I turn on the radio and get one of these twenty-four hour news stations. The weather report is good and they're rioting in Africa and the stock market opened up higher this morning and . . . 'arrested in attempted Wall Street bank robbery . . .' and I'm all ears, I turn the volume up : 'Shortly before eleven o'clock this morning, police report two men entered the Wall Street branch of the Irving Trust Company and attempted to rob it. Bank Guard James Moran, sixty-three, tried to stop the robbery and was shot in the chest. He's in fair condition at Beekman Downtown Hospital. The alleged bank robbers, Santo Mora, forty-one, and Pasquale Ardito, thirty-seven, are being held pending arraignment on attempted bank robbery charges, felonious assault, and attempted murder . . . And, in San Francisco, authorities reported . . .' I snap off the radio and say to Nancy, 'They sent those guys to make me there in the bank. Well, now Butch knows we didn't get it and he's madder than hell and cursing and sending guys looking for us all over the place.'

And I'm thinking, it's good that I heard that about the bank. It reminds me that we got to be careful. I got a pair of sunglasses on and some clothes that make me look like an apple, and I been feeling good here and lulled into being comfortable, you know, but this fella tells me again, 'Hey, wake up you damn fool! You think these people forgot about you?' No, they ain't forgot and they're not going to forget, ever, until they get me. So I got to always act like Butch was right around the corner or in that car that's coming up fast behind us.

I remember driving up this way to Buffalo one time with Butch on a score to hit somebody for the mob. The Old Man sent us as a favor to the Man in Buffalo. And we were younger and it was before the Thruway was built and Butch is driving like a maniac and I'm telling him, 'Slow down, you might get us a ticket,' and he laughs at me and says, 'If a cop ever puts his head in here I'll blow his brains out!' And we didn't get stopped but I'll always remember what a crazy man he could be. When Butch is that way there's no arguing with him; he just goes ahead and does what he wants like a bull. And this vicious and crazy-minded bastard is hunting for us, leading the hunt, you know?

But I can't help feeling relaxed because it's so beautiful and I got my baby and my stash. Now it's getting late in the afternoon and I think we better stop somewhere along here. We're off the Taconic and onto the Thruway which takes us around most of Albany, and I figure we ought to stop in Schenectady or Amsterdam or one of those places in between. So we get off the Thruway and onto a side road around Schenectady and we're looking for two things, a shopping center and a nice, small motel. We're still wearing the blue levi clothes we had on this morning and we need something sportier. So we find a big shopping center right off the highway there and go to the department store they have and I pick myself out some sports clothes so I look like a Hey Rube, a hick or whatever you call them. And we go to the women's department and she picks out some beautiful stuff, some short shorts and some slacks that really fit, you know what I mean? I had forgotten how beautiful she is and how much I really love her. When I seen her parading around in them clothes there I see how beautiful she is, inside and outside. I mean how great she is to stay with me through all this mess. So anyway, we get what we need and I'm all decked out in a loud flowery shirt and blue shorts and I'm really feeling good.

We mosey down the road, taking it easy, and come to a nice looking resort-type motel that has a little golf course connected with it and it's off the road to Utica that we got to take tomorrow. It's now about six o'clock and we take a shower together and enjoy ourselves. We come out and I say, 'I think I'm going to lie down for a little while.'

'I think that's a tremendous idea,' says Nancy, and she jumps in the bed after me and we make love for an hour or two. And when we get up we're starving, so we decide to go out and look the town over a little bit. We're going to stay away from every place that's connected, so we just take a ride around and look and come back to the motel. I'm doing this because I'm very leery of everything, naturally. So, we eat at the motel and Nancy cleans up my shoulder, and she patches it up again. I'm feeling terrific but now I'm tired, so we go back to bed and go to sleep holding each other.

The next morning I wake up and the sun is shining there and Nancy is looking beautiful – and my head feels like someone is burning holes in it. I got a wicked headache that won't quit, and while we're eating it's driving me wild; I can hardly talk. I take half a dozen aspirins and they don't do a thing. We cut out of the motel and Nancy's driving and we're down the highway twenty miles or so and I'm laying back in the seat with my eyes shut and not saying anything. I can't think of nothing but my head. She don't know what to do except find a doctor, but I can't do that. She says, 'When's the last time you had a headache like this?' and I say, 'The last time was in the can and I could do nothing about it and it took three days to let up.' And I'm thinking that this time I don't have three days to spare – I got to be sharp. I remember that what I did before sometimes when I got a real bad one was go to my Aunt Santie, who's sort of a Sicilian witch and she always cured me. So, I says, 'Nancy, we got to stop in Utica and find me an old woman to do the thing with oil and water.'

We argue a little about it. Nancy don't believe in that stuff, but she says okay and we take the turnoff to Utica. At the edge of town I tell her to stop at this phone booth and look in the book under a lot of Italian names – you know, Caruso and Fubini and Camorra and Manfredi and whatever – and see if she can pick out some streets where a lot of them live and that way we'll find the Italian neighborhood. And sure enough we do find where the Italians live and Nancy drives over to the other side of town and we're passing little bakeries and sausage stores and all that and I'm looking for an old woman, any old woman. And then I see three of them sitting outside a little newspaper store and we stop and I go up to these ladies very polite and ask them in Sicilian how everything is going and then I get around to asking them if they know of someone who can do the *malochia* for me. I tell them I'm in great pain and someone is trying to hurt me. And they look at me and turn and whisper a bit and one of them looks up and shakes her head yes. She's dressed in black like they all are, and like a lot of Italian ladies she has a couple of gold teeth and her hair is white and back in a bun with a big hairpin through it. So she says she lives upstairs three doors down and she'll be glad to help me. I tell Nancy to wait in the car and I follow the old lady.

And we get to the top of the stairs and into the old lady's room and it's dark in there with all this old furniture and she turns to me and says in Sicilian, 'Do you believe? Do you believe? Because if you don't believe, don't sit down.' And, naturally, I tell her that I believe all the way, and she sits me down there at a little round table in the middle of the room. She goes into the kitchen and comes back in a minute with a large china bowl full of water and she puts this down on the table. She tells me to concentrate and look into the water. And she has a little whiskey shotglass full of olive oil and holds it over the water for a minute and just three, four drops of oil come off her fingers and fall in the water. She's saying some ancient Sicilian prayers and they sound like a mumble to someone else. And she raises the bowl and holds it over my head and blesses me.

And she brings the bowl down and puts it back in front of me and – I know it's not my imagination because I seen it done before – the oil comes together and forms two big eyes on the water and beneath them three, four other big drops in a row and one small drop at one side. It's amazing, you know. Oil is supposed to spread out on water. And the old lady says, 'Now these two eyes are *la garonja,* the evil eye, and three people have got the evil eye on you, they want you dead. I don't know why. I don't know who they are, one is dark and one is old and . . .' She goes on to describe what sounds to me like Butch, the Old Man, and a guy named Joe Rocco who works for Butch.

'Now, you know who's after you?' she says to me.

'Yes, *mamarana,* I do.' And I really do know, I can see them right now cursing me and saying, 'That son-of-a-bitch, I hope he dies, I hope he gets pains in his head, I hope he dies.'

And she says, 'Listen, are you sick or something?'

'What do you mean?'

'Well,' she says, pointing to the little drop of oil, 'I show here where you been hurt there very badly lately.'

'I haven't been feeling good,' I say. I'm not going to tell her I been shot.

And, she says, 'Now that you understand it, I'll wash it away,' and she takes a pinch of salt and throws it in the bowl and all this oil breaks up on the water and there's no drops left and she says some more prayers and makes some signs around the bowl and picks it up and goes back to the window and throws the water out into the garden in the back. That way, the evil spirit wouldn't be in her house.

And as I'm watching the old woman throw the water I suddenly realize that my headache is gone.

I know she probably won't take no money so I slip a twenty under the placemat on the table there and I get up to go. Then the old woman comes back. She's only about five feet high, and she looks up at me and she says she's glad I came to her for help and then she makes a sign at me and says, 'Be careful of your car, I see danger in your car.' And that's that. I leave the room and go downstairs, wondering how I can explain all this to Nancy.

We get to Buffalo late that night and take the beltway around it to Niagara Falls and we pick out a mediocre-type hotel, an old joint that's been there since the twenties, nothing to rave about, because I know the better places are all owned by mob-connected people and are frequented by the same kind of guys, especially in the Buffalo-Niagara Falls area. Big Steve Maggadino is up here, and Louis Greco from Montreal has a lot of his guys up here, and Don Zerilli from Detroit is also here. It's a dangerous area in a way, but I feel sure we can get over the border with no problems. All we got to do is keep a low profile.

The next morning, Nancy's waking me up and saying, 'Come on, honey, let's go for breakfast.' And I smile and say, "That sounds like a hell of an idea.' So we take our showers and get cleaned up. I put on a pair of nice white slacks with a loud-colored shirt and a pair of white loafers and really look like a Hey Rube with a camera

202

thrown over my shoulder. Nancy puts on a black top and a pair of white shorts that won't quit and God bless her, she's the type that don't ever have to wear underwear, top or bottom, because she has got every brick in the right place, and I'm just looking at her thinking, 'Why did I ever get married? Why didn't I hook up with this one right off the bat?'

Anyway, we go out and have some breakfast and she looks like she's never been so happy in her life. I figure I owe her this much at least, I owe her the rest of her life to be good if we can enjoy it, if we can only get away from these animals and the government to boot. So, just like a couple of honeymooners, we're hand-in-hand looking at the falls, taking the elevator down below the falls and the boat where you have to dress up in yellow slickers and rain hats and, wow, she looks great with her face all wet. And we go around to all the tourist shops and I buy some dumb junk there, a plastic model of the falls and a knife-sharpening stone.

Come early afternoon, around three-thirty or so, we're getting hungry and we decide to go into a little local place and get a sandwich or something. It's nothing elaborate, but there's a bar and everything is done in brown stain, even the booths. So, we take a booth and the waitress is an old basil type, you know, with a cigarette butt hanging from the edge of her mouth. The bartender is up there in a T-shirt with an apron on and there's a couple of guys at the bar and another couple at a table. So there's maybe seven people at the bar and another eight or ten in the place. By this time we're both starving anyway, after making love last night and getting all that fresh air in from them waterfalls and all that business. We're really hungry and we're feeling good and we're relaxed there in the booth and we look at the menu. I decide to have a hamburger with some French fries and onion rings and a small beer and Nancy decides she wants the same only with no beer, a Coke or something like that. And she says, 'Johnny, I'm going to the ladies' room.' And she gets up and I'm watching and boy, when she walks it is really something from the backside. Whew, the way she moves, you know, I mean I'm sure you've heard that song, 'The Way You Move, Baby.' Well, it must have been written about her. And, the funny part about it, from the front side she looks just as good juggling around there, she's wearing no underwear like I said before. I don't notice it then but there's a couple of guys at the bar that are half in the bag that have been watching her. I got my back to the bar and she's been facing it and she's more or less ignoring them, naturally, though one's been winking at her and making motions. She pays no attention, she's used to that. She grew up in a tough neighborhood and worked in these B-joints as a dancer and a drink hustler and so she pays them no mind, which is the smart thing to do.

On the way back from the ladies' room, one of the guys at the bar makes a crack to her that catches my attention. He says, 'Hey, big chest!' or something like that. And she don't even pay no attention, she just keeps walking with that strut of hers that anyone would be happy to watch. She sits down in the booth and I say, 'What did that guy say to you?'

'Now, honey,' she says, 'don't let it bother you. Don't pay no attention to him. I couldn't care less if that man lives or dies, so whatever he says isn't going to mean anything to us.' Well, I'm trying to button up my tongue right now because I'm saying to myself, 'Look at this shit I have to take.' I'd like to get up and break this empty beer bottle over the guy's head for even considering looking at Nancy. And I'd like to take the broken bottle and use it on the creep's face, change his appearance so he don't ever try and be a ladies' man again. I can feel the blood pounding in my head at this, and I flash back to the old days when Nancy walked in any place that I was and people looked at her with respect because they were afraid to look at her in any other way. They would never make a comment to her because at that time I was the king of the pile and anybody foolish enough to try and get next to Nancy would be in serious, serious trouble and would probably end up in the hospital.

So, anyway, I'm saying to myself, 'Nancy's right. Let me just keep my mouth shut. We'll have our lunch here and we'll get the hell out because the best I could do is end up in a beef over her and maybe in real trouble.' And so I'm sitting back here relaxing and the next thing I know here comes this big jerk and he's drunk and he's a big bugger, but that don't make no difference. He don't even look at me, he just says to Nancy, 'Hey, honey, how about me and you having a drink?'

And she looks up and says, 'Why don't you go on your way, buster. Take a walk. Be a nice boy, no one's looking for trouble here.' And the guy just stands there looking down at her.

'Listen,' I says, 'what's the matter with you, pal? Are you crazy? Can't you see this is my wife I'm sitting with her? Why don't you go and mind your business?' And the guy says nothing and he's standing there, and I'm putting my hands down getting ready to jump up and bop him one and Nancy raises her hand as much as to say, I can handle this jerk. And, the next thing you know, the guy pushes in right next to Nancy in the booth and she's saying, 'Will you please get out of here before I call the police?'

Feeling like a creep, I say, 'Yeah, you better get out of here, or we're going to call the cops.'

'I don't give a fuck!' he says. 'The police are my friends.' And he's leaning over towards Nancy, who's now sitting way back in the corner of the booth. 'My God! Ah, gee, what a build you got on you, you bitch...'

And the guy is so in the bag he can hardly talk and he looks like he's starting to pass out, but he's just leaning over and he puts his hand right down between Nancy's legs and them shorts and grabs a hold of her just like an animal. This breaks the camel's back. She hits him in the face and I jump up and yell, 'You rotten, fucking, whoring bastard,' and I smash him on the head with a beer bottle. The guy is bleeding and I push him out of the booth and he hits the floor. His friend jumps off a bar stool and runs over and I get out there and he throws one and I kick him in the nuts and they're both down and I grab a chair and start beating them as hard as I can and, Nancy's trying to pull me away and get me out of there, but I don't see her and can't hear her. All I want to do is beat these fucks until they're raw meat.

The next thing I feel is a sharp pain in my bad shoulder. The goddamn bartender has run over with a billy club and is trying to bash my skull. He misses and hits me where it really hurts, and I'm down with red spots in front of my eyes. Someone must have called the cops because they get there a few minutes later just as I'm standing up and Nancy is trying to push me to the door. They see the locals on the ground and me standing and the next thing they're grabbing me by both arms and I'm swinging and yelling, 'It wasn't my fault.'

'Leave him alone!' Nancy's screaming at them. 'Leave him alone!'

And the cops, they know from nothing. 'You're going to jail, partner,' one of them says. 'You know you don't come up here from wherever you're from and beat up our folks around here. Who the hell you think you are?' And they snap the cuffs on me and I find myself in the back of a squad car with one of them asking me my name and address.

'I'm not going to tell you nothing,' I say. It's not that I'm trying to be a standup guy, it's that I'm afraid to tell these cops my name or anything else. They could be in the bag.

'You don't tell us nothing,' says the cop, 'and you're not even going to see the judge. We can't book you unless we know your name.'

'Okay,' I says, 'my name is Frank Carpi,' and I show them the driver's license and birth certificate and social-security card that the government got for me when they relocated me in Arizona. And we get to the police station and these guys haul me in the back and they're taking my fingerprints and I'm trying to pull away. I say, 'You got no right doing this. I didn't do anything wrong. Go ask the people at the bar.' And the cop tells me to shut up and stop moving around or he's going to lay me out and then print me.

Meanwhile, Nancy comes to the police station in a cab, tells me to quiet down and then leaves while they're booking me for assault and battery and possession of a deadly weapon – the chair. And five minutes later, clang, I'm locked in a cell and sitting there wondering what the hell to do. I'm beginning to imagine that Butch knows exactly what lock up I'm in and will be there in a few hours with a hit team.

Maybe an hour or two passes this way and I'm getting really uptight when suddenly the door down the hall opens up and a cop comes in with Nancy in tow and he opens up and lets me out. And we go back to where they booked me and one of the cops that pulled me in apologizes and says it was all a mistake and I say, 'Fine, just give me my stuff and let me get out of here. No hard feelings,' and I put on a big smile and hug Nancy.

Outside in the car, I ask her what she had to do to arrange that, guessing it had to cost three, four big ones. And she says, 'Guess again. It cost a smile and some tears.' And she tells me that she went back to the bar looking for the guy with the split head, but he was gone, they'd taken him to the hospital, but the other one was there and she walked up to him and says, 'Listen, this was our honeymoon, we were in here and my husband's been thrown in jail and we done nothing wrong but protect ourselves. Your friend was drunk. We didn't mean to hurt him, he meant to hurt us.'

And the guy says, 'You know something, you're right.'

'Gee,' says Nancy, a few tears coming into her blue eyes, 'if you feel that way, why don't you go down and tell the police how it really happened? Maybe they'll let him go so we can finish our honeymoon.' And you know, looking like she did, very few men could resist her, so the guy agrees and he goes to the hospital to see his friend who's been sobered up by the disinfectant they put on his head and he says, 'Look, I'm sorry. Just as soon as I get finished here I'll go down and drop the charges against your husband.' And the guy turns out not to be so bad when he's sober, and he's feeling bad about messing up a young bride's honeymoon and, sure enough, he comes to the station and tells them what happened and the captain on duty decides to turn me loose.

Now, we're free again and Nancy's very proud about having done it all by herself and I laugh and tell her how great she is and hug her and kiss her. And all the time my stomach is like ice. It just don't make any sense that they turn me loose so easy. I broke a couple of heads and I smashed a chair back there and now everybody is all smiles. If she'd have pieced them all off with big ones I could buy them burying the whole thing. But, this way, with a few tears and a wiggle of her behind. I don't believe it. So, I'm driving along slow and my mind is racing. They took my prints back there and they're on the way to Washington and when they hit the FBI, bells are going to ring. When the government gave me a new name they put a red tag on my file in Washington so that a fingerprint check would get back that I was Frank Carpi, harmless guy who once stole a car. But, since I dropped out of the system and broke parole they must have knocked the tag off and the word that comes back now is that I'm Johnny Forza, bad guy on the lam, wanted for this and that. They don't say shoot on sight, but they say I'm one of the most wanted, not only by them but by the mob. And then I realize they not only took my prints, they mugged me too. They won't send the picture to Washington, but what's worse it'll go to Albany by wire and the big crime computer there takes one look and yells back who I am and that Captain knows the mob is after me so he calls a certain number – you know Maggadino owns this town – and they tell him to let me go. So, they smile and say it was all a mistake and now we're boxed in but good – and I don't know what the hell to do.

It's after midnight when we get back to the hotel and I try not to seem upset, but when we get to the room I'm about ready to tell Nancy I'm feeling itchy and we should go over the border right now. Before I get around to saying it, she lies down on the bed and drops to sleep almost immediately. Now, without telling her what's worrying me, there's no way I can get her in gear to move this minute. It just don't make sense to run in the middle of the night unless you realize that the mug shots and prints might blow me out of the water. So I sit down and pull my shoes off and have a smoke and I'm thinking some more and I guess my nerves is getting the better of me. If the mob knew where I was they'd have picked us up right outside the police station. Why take a chance that we'd give them the slip? Nothing's going to happen tonight, but we better get out of here at the crack of dawn before the cops come to work in the records bureau. So, I pick up the phone and tell the clerk to call us at six-fifteen in the morning.

I toss and turn all night. I know I sleep some, but I roll over so much that in the morning the chains on my

209

cross and miraculous medal are tied in knots. All I could think of, laying there in bed, is rooms full of file cabinets and computers spitting out cards and mug shots coming over the wire and how the hell can I possibly escape all this? So I toss and turn and get up and get a drink of water and Nancy's sleeping like a baby. She thinks all our troubles are over and maybe they are. Maybe I'm just building trouble out of nothing. You know, it's an old Sicilian habit to expect the worst out of everything, because you don't get disappointed that way. I think the dawn is never coming and the next thing I know the phone rings and I jump out of my skin.

So we get up and I call down for breakfast to be sent up while we get dressed and start packing and I go down to the lobby to pay our bill and there's a cop standing there talking to the desk clerk. I don't act scared, I just walk up to the counter and the cop turns and nods and leaves. There's a squad car outside the front door and he gets in it and takes off. I never seen the guys before, but I get a funny feeling. And then I get a worse feeling : what difference does it make that the police records bureau isn't open all night? That fucking computer in Albany never sleeps and here this guy is on duty and it's not eight o'clock yet.

When we get in the car I begin thinking that maybe we ought to head south and into the Pennsylvania mountains, somewhere we could hole up. But, it's a bright, sunny day and there's no one around and I'm thinking that all this worry is for nothing. It's only a few miles down the road to the border and if Butch was here he'd never let us get a block away. So, I'm taking it nice and slow. I been in trouble before and I'm not scared kid ; I'm not going to blow it by letting a guard think I'm nervous. The only worry is that it's only a matter of time before the law finds out who I am, and when they do, they're going to know they want me – and Butch'll probably know it too. So what I got to worry about right now is a phone call to the border while we're crossing or some guy in uniform standing there waiting for us.

We get to the river and there's the bridge with signs pointing to Canada and saying that the Thruway now becomes Queen Elizabeth Way. There's a couple cars there ahead of us but they seem to move them through pretty fast. And we come to the U.S. gate house and the guy bends down, looks at us and says, 'Okay, folks.' And we move across the bridge. On the other side, the man wants to see our identification and hear our names. Nancy gives her right name and shows a driver's license; I use Carpi and my fake birth certificate. And everything's fine with him, too and he says, 'Sir, the main road ahead, route four-oh-five, is under repair for the next two hours. Please take the first right you come to. You'll wind up back on four-oh-five in about ten miles.' And he salutes and I thank the guy and drive past and – Jesus Christ, we're home free. I start down the road and reach over and grab Nancy and she's laughing and crying at the same time. I can't believe we finally made it. I want to stop somewhere and get drunk. This is going to be a great night.

I'm driving along and it's like we're flying. The sun is shining and the grass is green and the road is empty and there's nothing to stop us. In a few hours we'll be up in the farm country and no one will know us for a thousand miles. I'm feeling a little dizzy. Being in the clear with Nancy and the stash is like winning the lottery. I want to yell and laugh and my head is running like a movie with pictures of beaches in Acapulco, Nassau and Rio. I'm thinking of when we were down in Antiqua in the West Indies and we're staying in this little broken down motel because the island was loaded with conventioneers who had no place to stay. All by ourselves and it was great. And we'd just lay around on the beach all afternoon and have some fruit drinks and the little native boys would go out and catch some fresh lobsters right off the water and give them to the chef for us and he would boil them up and make some nice lobster salad and we would just lounge around and hug each other and make love to each other and walk on the beach like a couple of apples. And we would sit in the sand looking at that warm green water down there. Watching the pelicans dive every once in a while and come up with a fish. Beautiful.

Down the road a couple hundred yards we come to a right turnoff, a two-lane blacktop, and I take it and wonder why there's no detour sign pointing this way. I slow down. And I'm getting this funny feeling you get when there's something wrong and you don't know what it is. Since I beaned that guy with a bottle and got collared it's been like we can do no wrong, all these guys bowing and scraping like someone told them to make it real easy for us.

Half a mile beyond the bridge, we're still taking it slow, and seeing signs for something called St Catharines but it's woodsy here like back on the parkway in New York. Beautiful. And we come to a detour sign in the middle of the road with a guy standing there waving a little red flag and pointing to a side road. I wonder if it's on the up and I say, 'Well, what do you think, Nancy, do we want the detour?'

'Well, nobody knows we're here yet,' she says, not thinking about the prints and photos. 'They couldn't possibly know, John.' So I take the right and cross the fingers of my left hand so she can't see, and I'm on a gravel road that winds through heavy trees and brush, and we get down two, three hundred yards and the road keeps bearing right there, back toward the river and I look in the rearview mirror and there's another car on the detour coming up fast behind us. So I speed up and a minute later I look ahead and there's another car coming slowly out of a little side road like he's waiting for me to pass.

And I smell what's going on. This is a squeeze play. I ought to know. I been in a few myself – on the other side of the squeeze.

So I reach down under the seat and grab my pistol and pull it out between my legs so I can get to it fast. Now, I know what happened. The bells did light up last night, but they didn't want to pull anything right there in town. They figured if we didn't see anything we'd come across the river and they could do it out in the woods with nobody around. Shit! If I'd only gone south last night. But, I know better than that. If I'd gone the other way a car would have tailed us and . . . I'm moving now and the car in front turns onto the road and comes towards me slow and, wham, there's a hole in the right side of the windshield, and it's so shattered I can't see out of it. They're shooting at us, and two more slugs hit the back of the car. And I yell at Nancy to hit the floor. The guy in front is moving at a walk and the one in back is picking up speed; they're going to try and sandwich me. They keep shooting and I stop short, turn the wheel right and floor it in reverse until we hit a tree and I'm going to start a run between them when I look at Nancy and she's leaning forward against the seat belt. I yell at her to wake up and pull her back by the arm. Her neck and dress are all blood. Her eyes are open and she can't see. I'm screaming her name and I flip the car in drive and move it as fast as she'll go, shooting out the window at the backup car, and I don't give a damn if I hit one of them or not. And I'm saying kid's prayers like I was five, 'Please, God, let us get out of this, let her out of this. She don't deserve this. Hail Mary, full of grace . . .'

I don't hit the car in front, I pass him so close that we're tearing chrome off each other, and I turn down the little side road he came out of, I don't care where it goes. A hundred yards, two hundred, three hundred and I can see sky ahead and I jam on the brakes – only forty feet from the guardrail overlooking the Niagara River.

I reach over and grab Nancy's arm and touch her face and she's a statue, she's not there, she's dead, and I'm crying for the first time since my father died, I can't see. I don't know how long I was that way. I open my eyes and I'm feeling cold now and I get out of the car and walk around behind it and suddenly I see that all the bullets hit on Nancy's side – not one on the driver's side. That couldn't be no accident. Those guys were using rifles, you know. And I get the picture now. They wanted to kill her, not me. You understand? Butch, that motherfucking *gornuda* bastard, had Nancy killed in front of my eyes just for revenge, just to make me suffer more before he kills me. I'm standing here shaking. I knew he was crazy mad, but I never seen anybody do a thing like this. He's turned into an animal, a mad dog that has got to be destroyed. So I get back in the car and I put it in reverse for about fifty feet, stop, open the door, grab the briefcase off the back seat and toss it out, floor the accelerator, and hold on. And I jump just before she hits and goes down, seventy, eighty feet into the river with Nancy, and everything. I'm running through the brush and I can hear a car coming down the road fast. They're going to be looking and I'm going to be gone. And when they leave I'm going back and pay a call on my old friend. And this time no one in the house will live.

# CHAPTER EIGHT

It seems like I been in the goddamn woods forever, sliding on leaves with mud all over my shoes. My heart is broken. I'm thinking about Nancy. Feel like I been whacked in the head and now I'm asking, 'Where the hell am I?' I mean, it's like I can't see nothing that tells me where I am. And what's worrying me is I know a guy could be fifty feet away with a deer rifle and I never see him, and – wham! – I get it in the back and he tells the game warden it was an accident. And maybe he don't even get arrested. Happens all the time. I can almost hear them saying, 'Gee, I'm sorry,' and 'Ain't it awful how many hunters get killed?' And they're shaking their heads. So, I look back over my shoulder and I'm walking a little faster. The river or the lake or whatever is over there, maybe twenty yards on the right. So I know I'm moving away from where I got ambushed. If I didn't have that to go by I could have walked right back there by now. It's easy to go in circles out here. I figure those guys are long gone, but I can't be sure they don't send another team out to poke around. And the cops or guys from the border have got to be looking for the car trying to find out if anyone's alive, because it must have been seen from the other side of the river. So I figure that right now Butch don't know if I'm dead or alive, and he's jumping up and down waiting to hear. All he knows is the car went over. If I'm dead, case closed. If I'm alive, I may be hurt or okay, but he's still got me to take care of.

So by now they probably send down a cop on a rope and he gives a quick look and in a couple hours Butch will know that I may be alive. He'll know they didn't find me in the car and I either got out before it went over or fell out after it went. And I think Butch is going to guess that I made it out of there and I'm loose somewhere. And, 'Hey!' I'm saying to myself, 'stop kidding yourself!' There's no way Butch is going to buy me going over into the river there. Too much like a hit, you see? Driver's out cold and you push the guy's foot on the accelerator, put the car in gear, and let her go over. Nobody buys that as an accident outside the movies. So Butch knows I'm here and running. Now, I'm very sure as soon as these guys report back, they get the word to come out here again. The only thing he still don't know is if I got the cash. And he won't find out until the cops haul the car out in a couple days. Right now, they're not even looking for money, you see. They don't know there was was any money. So Butch has got to look at it this way: if I got the cash I'm still running and he ain't ever going to see me again, but, if the cash is in the car when they get it up, there I got to come back to the States for another stash he don't know about – or I got nothing to come back for and I'm in a corner up here. Putting myself in Butch's shoes, he's going to figure that I got the money just the way I got it, by taking it with me before I sent the car over into the river. So, I'm betting he's going to think I am running like hell up north or for Western Canada.

Either way, Butch is going to have his pals up here in Canada on my trail. And, you know, that's the tough part. Canadian wiseguys are different looking. They ever dress more casual, tweeds and things like that. And that means I'm not going to find it so easy to spot them if they got the trains or the buses or airport covered. A guy I think looks like a wiseguy is going to turn out to be a tourist or an off-duty priest and the real one looks like a doctor going fishing.

You see, here I go, thinking about how I'm going to get

back to New York when I don't even know where I am or how to get out of here. Why am I thinking this way? Well, it's because I'm going back to kill Butch Lombardi. I'm very cool about it now and I don't know why. I can't explain it. It's just something that I got to do. I'm not crazy like back there in Brooklyn. I'm cold mad, you know? Ice-cold mad. I'm just going to find him and kill him like you'd step on a cockroach. I don't even want to torture the son-of-a-bitch now. I just want to see him dead.

Right now, I know I got to get rid of this stash. I mean park it somewhere safe so I can come back and get it when I'm done with Butch. I can't carry it with me or I'll lose it or somebody steals it. The first thing I think of is bury the damn briefcase. Dig a hole, cover it up and mark it some way so I know where to dig it up again. So I walk back and around and I find a nice place and I pick up a stick and get down on my knees and start on the hole. You ever try to dig with a stick? Can't be done in this kind of ground. Soon as you get under the dead leaves it's hard and full of roots and stones. So I'm down here hacking at the dirt and making too much noise and sweating and getting exactly nowhere. So what do I do now? I saw some big rocks back there aways. I could put the thing between two or three of them maybe, or roll a big one over and put the stash under it and roll it back and try and remember which rock it's under. And then it hits me that rocks are what kids play in and it would be my luck to have some kids fooling around tomorrow and come across the stash.

So I'm walking anyway and thinking and I guess I could toss the bag over the cliff on a rope, if I had a rope. But it'd be seen by somebody in the river or on the other side. Maybe in a hole in the gound made by a gopher or a mole or something. Fine, except I ain't seen such a hole and what if the animal ate the briefcase? I'm thinking and

217

thinking and I just don't have no ideas and I'm turning back the way I was going when a flash goes through my head. I think I remember a little shed right near the turn-off road where I drove down to the cliff. If it's a toolshed maybe they have shovels and rakes in there and I can dig a real hole and bury this stash. And, after what seems half an hour of walking I get back to the place and I don't hear nobody around and, sure enough, there's the shed. It's a little square building like as big as four phone booths and made out of corrugated tin. I get down and go on hands and knees around to the front of it and the door is padlocked, naturally, nothing I can kick through. There's an inch or so of space under the door and I'm feeling inside with my fingers when I also feel that the shed is up off the ground a little. It's sitting on cinder blocks, I guess, to keep the rain out.

I'm crawling back for the briefcase and it hits me : if I put the damn thing under this toolshed nobody ever finds it. There's grass and weeds growing up on all sides. You come up to the shed and it looks like it was sitting right on the ground. Even if you see it's on blocks, who the hell is going to look under it? A dog maybe. So I push the briefcase under the back of the shed with my foot, get it right under the middle so you wouldn't notice it even if the grass was gone. And then I'm pulling and whacking at the grass and weeds to make it look like no one's been messing around. The only thing I got to worry about is if they move the damn shed or a dog smells something. I get up and walk away and turn and look back. I think I can find this place again, too. I don't think I'll forget this turnoff as long as I live.

I know the longer I stick around here, the more danger there is that the boys from Montreal are going to come back and find me. So I'm walking along and I'm thinking that this road on my left here – I can't see it, but I know it's there – leads to St Catharines. It was the road I was driving on a couple hours ago, and there's got to be small towns between here and there. So, if I walk long enough I got to hit one. The only trouble is that they're going to figure that too. They know I can't call a cab out here and I can't hitchhike and I can't go back across the bridge into Buffalo on foot. I got to get a car or a bus and the first town I hit is going to be the place they stake out. I'm going to walk right into a trap. In fact, just because I'm walking and not driving is going to make it easy for them to spot me. They don't even need a picture. Walking is like wearing a bullseye on my back that says, 'Shoot me.' It's going to be like one of them Western movies where the guy walks down the street and there's a shootout. My problem is my gun's empty. Anyway, I'm walking slow now, and up ahead the woods seem to come to an end. Looks like there's another road running right through. But as I get closer I see it's not a road; it's a rest area where cars can pull off and people get out and look at the river. And I keep walking and, sure enough, I see a couple of cars and a camper there now – and, suddenly, I know that here's my ticket out of here.

I stop twenty feet inside the trees and wait. About ten minutes and one car cranks up and drives away. A few more minutes and the other car goes, leaving the camper. And I'm moving when – shit! Another damn car drives into the rest area. So I back up and sit down behind a tree and cross my fingers. And – a piece of luck – the new car doesn't stop long. Driver's got to piss or whatever he's got to do and, anyway, it leaves. So there's the camper, one of those big jobs that can carry four, five people and it's only a short ways from where the trees stop. So I get my gun in my hand, fold my coat over it, walk up to the door of the camper nonchalant-like, and knock. And nothing. I knock again. Door opens a slow crack, I put on a smile and, 'Say, my car broke down back there. Could I trouble you people for a lift?' Door opens and it's a woman. Nice body, late twenties, no makeup. She smiles. A man's voice from inside, 'Josie! What's the guy want?'

'Oh, George. It's all right. He needs a lift.' She smiles and shrugs at me, looks over her shoulder, 'His car broke down—' And he comes up behind her. Fat, older by fifteen, twenty years. 'Where's your car, mister?' He pushes the woman behind him. He's not as dumb as she thinks.

'Well, it's about a mile back towards the falls.' I'm acting very sincere. 'I think the water pump or whatever went—'

Guy says, 'Look, mister. I don't pick up hitchhikers, but I'll tell you what. I got a CB radio rig and I'll get on to the provincial police and ask them to help you. How's that?'

It's lousy, of course, so I ain't got no choice. I drop my coat and put the biscuit to his head. He don't know it ain't loaded. 'You are going to take me for a ride,' and I shove him inside and shut the door behind me. The guy's wife is sitting at the little table there with a kid, a boy about eight or nine. Cut, kind of on the small side, takes after his mother. So I'm telling the guy to sit down with his wife and he's running off at the mouth, you know. 'Take whatever you want. I haven't got much money with me, but ...'

'Shut up!' I give him the wiseguy talk. 'I don't want your fucking money. You're just going to take me for a ride. You understand?' The guy don't say nothing. He sits there staring at me.

'Listen,' I tell him, 'get in the driver's seat and wind this thing up. I want to go to Toronto Airport and don't break no speed limits or touch that radio. Move!' He fumbles with the starter but the engine don't catch. He's shaking. So I reach down and grab the radio microphone, rip it out, drop it and stomp on it. He starts the engine and drives out of the rest area and takes a right onto the highway. I sit down at the table, right across from the stove, and keep an eye on him while the lady and her kid stare at me wide-eyed. And we come to a town called Niagara-on-the-Lake and we're stopped at a light and I'm thinking it's dumb to sit up here in front where any cop outside can see me, so I get up to move to the back and the guy starts up so fast I almost take a header. I turn fast with the gun up and I pull the hammer back so's he can hear it click. I grab the kid by the arm and pull him with me onto a sofa that's halfway to the back of this thing and say, 'Listen, wiseass! I don't want no trouble with you. You take me over there and you mind your business...'

'But, ah, I ... I—' He's slobbering. 'I didn't mean ...'

'Shut your mouth or I shut it for you!' I'm yelling at him. 'Anything goes wrong, you trying flashing your lights, you try anything smart — and I kill the kid.' I won't kill the kid. I'm no animal and I hate to hurt suckers, but I'm mad enough to sound like I mean it. So the guy shuts up and drives and his wife is sitting there at the table with her eyes shut. And I look down and the kid is looking at me : he studying me and he ain't afraid. I look away, turn around and pull up the window curtain a little so I can see out, and I look back at the kid and he's still looking at me. And, I don't know why but I find myself smiling at the kid as much as to say, 'Don't worry. Nothing's going to happen to you.' And he looks at me for a minute and then looks away, and I'm wondering if maybe I did something dumb and trying to figure why I did it.

Well anyway, we're on a superhighway now, zipping along about sixty, and I got to fight to stay awake. It's warm in here and the sofa is comfortable and I need some coffee and a cigarette. And I'm going to ask the kid to fix me some coffee when I suddenly think I don't want anyone messing around with boiling water in this place. This kid could have seen too many cowboy movies and might try and play here, so I have him get me a coke instead and I light up. I ain't never been in a camper before, and it's pretty nice, sort of laid out like a boat. Reminds me of the cruiser I had, a fifty-five foot Chris-Craft I bought a few years back. I called it the *Ebbtide* and we really used to have some great times on that boat. Take it out fishing or just for a run on Long Island Sound. We even used it for sit-downs a few times; it's impossible to bug a boat so that you can hear people talking on deck in a wind, you know. I kept it at City Island. I used to dream about getting a boat big enough to live on and just sailing away out of sight one day and changing the name on the boat and disappearing.

We been on this road more than an hour now and I look out the window and we're getting into the motel-and-roadhouse part of Toronto, and I move up to the table in front and tell the guy to pull off at the next exit. He pulls off and I tell him to go back a ways and we come to a bunch of motels and I pick the one with the parking lot that's the most empty. I have him park this thing near the motel office and I stand up to leave and grab the kid's arm again. 'Listen,' I say, 'I'm going inside there with your kid. No trouble. Remember.' And we get out and I slam the door. There's nobody in the office but the girl behind the counter. I tell her my friends outside want a room for the night, because they're tired of camper life, and me and my son here want a cab to the airport. The girl says we can take the airport courtesy car and while she's calling for it I pick up a book of matches that has this motel's phone number on it. And the kid and I sit down in the office and wait. In fifteen, twenty minutes or so, a green Chevy van skids to a stop in front and the driver hops out. I tell the kid to get in and I go over to the camper. Inside the guy and his wife are sitting together on the sofa and she's crying. He sees me and starts to get up. I can see he's mad as hell so I quiet him down.

'Look,' I say, 'I'm taking your kid with me . . .' And the lady is about to start yelling so, I say, 'And if you open your mouth, if anyone comes near me, I'll kill him on the spot. I don't care. When I get where I'm safe I let your kid loose and he calls you at this motel. So, you better get in there and take a room and wait by the phone.' I back out and then I see an open closet right in front of me with a lot of clothes and a couple of bags. And I just reach over and pick up a small suitcase, like the kind you can put under a seat, and it feels empty and I take it and slam the door and climb in the van. The driver comes back and we're off.

At the airport, I tell the guy to drop us at Air Canada. We go up to the counter and I tell the girl I want two first-class seats on the next plane to Newark for John Corso and son Robert, which is the kid's first name. She tells me Air Canada don't go to Newark and we'll have to try Allegheny. So we walk down the terminal and I can tell the kid is upset. Until just now, he don't know I was going to take him on a plane ride, and he's getting uptight. I can feel it in his hand. So, I stop and take him over to an empty bench right there in the middle of this place and sit him down and say, 'Listen Robert, I'm not going to kill you if you try running or yelling for help – but I'll whack you so hard you'll never forget it.' And while he's thinking about that, I tell him, 'You know, Robert, if you was to go running up to that guard over there and yell that I was trying to kidnap you, he'd never believe it.' The kid looks up at me like I must have read his mind, and I say, 'I'd just go and grab you and tell him you're a little nuts or something, and you go to a special school for kids that are soft in the head.' And he thinks about that for a minute and it looks to me like I got to him. Fact is, they most likely wouldn't believe him – kids are always saying crazy things – but I'd just as soon not have him try. Anyway, the kid gets up and we walk down towards the

Allegheny ticket counter, and on the way I stop at a drugstore and tell him to pick out some magazines and candy. Right inside the door there's a big trash barrel with a swinging top and while he's looking over there I put the suitcase down and bend over and open it a little and make like I'm checking something and look around to see who can see me – and slip my gun into the trash barrel. I know the Customs guys don't check too careful between Canada and the States, but I might be unlucky and an empty gun is a piece of junk anyway. At Alleyheny, I buy the tickets and we go through the customs place there and no one looks at the bag and I check it through. Robert seems to have calmed down a bit : he's reading a magazine about outer space. The tickets come to $151.20 and there's a flight in forty minutes. And I'm standing there looking at the kid and I'm suddenly worrying about his folks. That guy is nutty enough to call the cops so I better give him something else to think about, you know? The minute you leave a sucker like that too long he's going to figure out something cute. Also, I got to jolly this kid along so he thinks this is fun like running away from home. And I say, 'Hey ! Robert. I don't want your ma to be worried. Maybe you call her and tell her you're okay. But don't tell her where you are? If she finds out, it's big trouble.' So, we go across there to a phone booth and get inside together and I dial the number of the motel and give him the phone.

'Mrs Wallace, please.' The kid clears his throat. 'They checked in a little while ago . . .' And he's waiting, waiting, and 'Hello? Hello? Mother?'

'Yes, I'm okay and . . .'

'No ! No, Mother, don't do that !' I can hear her yelling on the other end of the phone and he's still talking to her, 'I'll call again later and you can do that. Okay? Okay, Mom? . . . Come on, Mom. Take it easy. I'll call you later and then – Don't. Don't worry. I'm going to be fine . . . Mom! I'm going to be okay. Really. But I got to go now . . .'

I push the thing that hangs up and he puts the phone on the hook there, and 'You did good, Robert.'

'Uh huh.' He's looking at me funny.

'I mean, I wanted you to keep your ma from getting too upset, you know?' I'm finding it hard to talk to this kid now.

'She knew we're at the airport because she saw the van before. She was going to call the police,' he tells me, just like that.

'Going to what?' I grab his arms.

'She was going to tell them you're at the airport with me.'

'Did she? Did she call them?' I'm shaking him and looking all around. This phone booth feels like a fishbowl or the wrong end of a shooting gallery.

'I think I talked her out of it,' he says to me, smiling a little. And I'm thinking he better have talked her out of it or I'm done for. So I grab the kid's hand and walk him back fast to where the flight is boarding. Inside the plane I'm as jumpy as a cat waiting for the damn thing to take off and worrying that a squad of cops is going to come rushing in here with guns in their hands. Now, they're closing the door and it's going to be okay in a couple of minutes – and they're stopping. The door is opening a little. One more passenger, a big guy, comes sliding in and says a few words to the girl up there and she points to the back and now he's walking past me looking at seat numbers. Or is he looking at me? This guy is the size of a cop and he could be sitting there now, a few rows behind me, and when we're in the air he could stick a gun to my head and put the cuffs on me. I'm sure that's how they'd do it. Wait a minute, I'm thinking, if this bird was a cop he would have collared me right off. So, maybe the guy is a marshal. He has that look about him and he could be one

225

that Mister Oakes put on my tail to make sure that I don't
make another try for Butch. Mister Oakes would not
care about what I done so far. I mean, I'm the one that's
been hurt. But he's not going to let me try again for Butch.
The girl is asking us if we want something to drink and a
little snack and kid asks for a Coke and I tell her I'll have
a beer. And I'm sitting here asking myself why was I such
a jerk to let this kid call his people. I know why I did it. I
wanted to simmer them down a bit and I wanted to get
this dumb kid on my side a little so he don't do anything
crazy like write a note to the pilot. And I look over at him
and I'm wondering to myself, how do you talk to a kid like
this? You know, I never talked to one except to say,
'Hey you! Catch!' and throw him my car keys. I mean
there were kids around the neighborhood that used to
watch cars, look out for strangers when we was sitting
down to dinner there with the Old Man. All that kind of
thing. But those were street kids, you know? Kids like I
was at that age, always looking to do things for wiseguys,
to get close to them. So I'm trying to think of how to
talk and I say to myself, 'Robert, ah'... Bobby ... Ah,
can I call you Bob?' And this goes on and I'm feeling
like Mickey the Dunce. Why the fuck should I care what
this kid thinks of me?

I figure the kid knows from nothing about the street,
so I talk to him like I would any sucker. I turn around and
say, 'Look, Robert. What do you think is going on here? I
mean, who do you think I am and what is all this?'

He shakes his head, 'Gee, I don't know.'

'Would you like to know?'

'Well, yeah. I guess so.' He's not sure he wants to play
in this game. So I stop and look at him for a minute and
say, 'What I'm going to tell you is the God's honest truth.
But you're going to have trouble believing it.' Now, I got
the kid's attention for sure and I stop again. I'm feeling
like I do when I'm setting up some apple to be clipped,

and the funny thing is I'm doing this because I really want the kid to like me.

'When I came to your camper, I'd just been shot at by some guys that was trying to kill me.'

'Gee,' the kid says. He's amazed and I'm thinking this is dumb for me to tell anybody, even him.

'And,' I tell him, 'the lady I was going to marry was killed by them guys.'

'Gosh, that's awful.'

And I'm thinking about Nancy now, and I know I'm going to cry if I don't keep talking, so I say, 'I was walking out of the woods and scared – scared about those guys finding me again and I needed a ride out of there. If you'd given me a ride to town I'd have never pulled my piece and taken over. I didn't want to do this, Robert. I swear I had no choice.' I'm sounding like a Boy Scout or a priest.

'But – but, why didn't you call the police?' he asks me. 'I mean if they shot at you?'

This is the hard part. 'Look, Robert. I'm sort of a bad guy myself, or I used to be. I come from a poor family, lousy neighborhood, started stealing when I was your age. Never went past tenth grade.' All true, I'm thinking, but bullshit as far as why I am what I am. 'I stole stuff from stores and whatever', I'm telling him. 'Anyway, I was in the joint – you know, prison – and I went with the government and testified against some guys they was trying to send up. And Uncle Sam said, "Okay, you paid your debt. You're a free man," you see?' And the kid nods.

'But,' I tell him, 'friends of the guys I put away is after me and some of the cops are in the bag, you know, cops that take money to do the wrong thing.' And, I just lost the kid and I can tell by his eyes that he don't believe that bit about the cops, which is right for a sucker. They all think they can square a traffic ticket, but cops don't really take money from the mob. I know this kid's still buying the cops on the TV shows. So I'm sitting here drinking my beer and wondering why the hell I'm talking so much.

Now, the kid has a Coke and he's reading a magazine and I'm thinking he could have been a kid like I could have had, if things worked out right. And I'm starting to feel bad again, so I say, 'Look, I'm on my way back to New York to get the guy that's been trying to kill me and when I get him I don't care what happens to me. They can kill me, put me back in the can, I don't care about nothing anymore.' And he's staring at me, so I ask him straight out, 'What would you do if you was me?'

He looks down and looks up and says, 'Well, I don't know, maybe I'd do the same thing. I don't know.' And I smile at him. This is a pretty spunky kid. He's not scared. He listened and he's not going to agree with me all the way. So, that's that and the 'Fasten Seatbelt's sign goes on. We're coming into Newark. It's only an hour-and-a-half flight and, suddenly, I'm thinking about the job I got to do now. It's like the last hours have been a vacation and now I'm back to work, you understand.

I'm starting to figure where Butch is right now, and that's not hard unless he's changed his whole schedule, which he would definitely not do on account of me. It would be a pain to switch it all around, and he would never admit that he'd had to do it on my account. If he did do it, every one on the street would know why he was doing it and he couldn't stand that. Also, it would mess up business cause people he meets every week would have to change their schedule too. So I'm going to assume that Butch is where he ought to be tonight. Which means I got to think about who's going to try and stop me from getting him. I can pretty much figure about Butch's people, but will the cops have him staked out? I doubt it, but the Feds might be around. I'm wondering about the FBI and then Mister Oakes's face comes into my head. Now, he knows I pegged a few shots at Butch's men down in

Philadelphia, and he probably knows about the thing at the bank. And, I'm thinking, he might even know about the car over the cliff by now. And if he knows about Nancy he may figure I'm coming back for Butch again and he might just try to stop me. Not that he cares if Butch gets it, but I think he does care if I get it or if they send me up for it. Now, I'd hate for Mister Oakes to be in the way when I start blasting Butch, and I'd hate to have him collar me before I get close. So I got to call him off, and the only way I know to do that is to get him on the phone and tell him I'm okay. I got to give him some kind of story he'll buy, something that'll make him think I'm not out to get Butch again. And that's not going to be easy. I lived with Mister Oakes for months and months, night and day. He knows me as well as anybody, maybe he knows me better, because he's the kind that notices what other guys might not notice.

Anyway, we land and I take the kid to the baggage claim and pick up the little suitcase I borrowed. And I keep an eye peeled for the guy who might be a marshal, but I don't see him. So, we're standing there and I hand him the suitcase and he looks a little surprised. 'Here's some money,' and I give him a couple of hundreds and the matchbook from the motel. 'Buy a ticket back to Toronto and use the change to call your folks. Okay?'

'Sure.' He's smiling now.

'Goodbye, Robert.'

'Goodbye, Mister Corso.' And he turns and starts walking over to the American ticket counter, and I yell, 'Wait a minute!' He stops and turns and I walk over, and I grab his arm. 'Listen, Robert, you been pretty smart so far. Don't screw it up now. You just take the money and go home and when you're there you can tell anybody anything you want. I don't care. Just don't do nothing foolish now, you know what I mean?' He's looking like he don't know what to say. 'Okay?'

'Okay.' He nods, but he's not smiling now. And I'm kind of sorry I have to talk to the kid this way, but he could still blow things for me. So I turn and walk down to where you go to get a taxi and when I get to the door I look back and the kid is still standing there. I wave to him and I'm out the door and into the first cab in line. And I shut the door and lean back and the driver starts moving and I look out the window and – Christ! I'm losing my marbles or I'm seeing Mister Oakes again. This time, he's sitting in a car parked right in front of the cab stand. We're picking up speed and I look back and I can't see through the windshield of his car to see if it is Mister Oakes and the car doesn't move and the driver of this cab is asking me where I want to go. So, I turn around and tell him to take me to Market Street in Newark. It's a skid-row section, and I pay him off near the train station and walk until I come to a big sporting-goods store. Inside, I tell the guy I want a twelve-gauge shotgun, double barrel. And he shows me a couple and I go through the motions of swinging them up and snapping the trigger and I finally pick out a Savage double and get two boxes of shells. I tell him I'm going after turkey so I want a box of number-two birdshot and, just in case I see a fox, a box of number-one buckshot, the size that holds a dozen thirty-caliber lead balls. From across a room it's like shooting a handful of rifle bullets all at once. The guy says number-two buck is better for foxes than number-one and I tell him not to give me an argument, so he shrugs and gives me the shells. I wanted to ask for double-O, but it's not the deer season and it would have seemed funny – ask for double-O and you might just as well ask for a riot gun. Guy's going to know I'm hunting something bigger than turkeys. Anyway, what the hell, from six or seven feet it don't matter what you got in a shotgun; it's all going to go anyway. So, the guy wraps it up for me and it comes to $319.73, and while he's putting string on the package I see a dark green army raincoat and try it on and tell him to add that to the bill. It's another twenty bucks and I keep it on instead of having him put it in a bag.

Down the street there's a big junky hardware store, just the kind I want. I get a hacksaw and three strong blades, a roll of electric tape, a big switchblade knife, a pair of work gloves, and a little can of oil. I go outside again and I'm near the Newark train station, but I'm not going to take a train to New York, not after last time. I get in a cab and tell the guy I want to go to that motel in Manhattan, I can't remember the name, on Tenth Avenue in the Fifties, way away from anything. And right smack in Butch's territory.

The driver takes off, and it's beginning to get dusky there. I'm looking at the New York skyline, the skyscrapers shining like they're on fire, and I'm feeling like I been away for years and it's only been two days. Two days! I can't believe all that's happened in a week. I think of Nancy and I can hardly stand the aching. It's like I lived a whole life in a couple days. And this day that's two-thirds over now may be the end of it for me. I got a chance to make it, but not much of a chance. I might luck out, but I'm not going to count on it. What I got to figure out now is just how I'm going to do this job. I'm thinking on it like the Old Man just give me the action and told me it was so important that he hoped I would take care of it personal and not round up any mechanics to do it or call in the hit squad. So here I am trying to think like a professional and it's been a few years since I did a job all by myself. Now, the professional thing is simple. It means I just don't go roaring up to the front door and try blasting through to Butch the hard way. But I can't stay around this town for long, so I don't have all the time in the world to find him and set him up right. I like to take a week or two and watch him, get his schedule down, but I got to hit him right now. No time at all. What I got to do is figure where he's going to be tonight and hit him where I got the best chance of getting close.

This is Tuesday, which means that Butch left his house a couple hours ago and went to the office. He might not be living at home these days because of the Forza problem – not, you understand, because he's afraid to be home because I might invade it, but because he's got a lot of duties on the business side that he's got to do every day. I just add to the workload and he might be living in his apartment just so he don't have to spend time driving home. He could even have a suite in one of them mob-connected hotels in mid-town there. Anyway, I'm thinking he left where he's living a few hours ago and he's probably now at the office. Unless he moved, the office is over a truck garage in the Thirties between Tenth and Eleventh Avenues. You'd never know from the outside, but his office in this crummy garage is like it was in a big mid-town skyscraper – nice furniture, paneled walls, a built-in bar, even a little bathroom with a shower.

Now, Tuesday is a busy night like Monday. You see, the weekend receipts get picked up early in the next week – all the bookmaking money, the loan-shark money, the dope money. It all comes in Monday and Tuesday nights, and Butch has got to be around to check it. He can't hand off that job. At least he won't hand it off. Now, tonight's Wednesday and the big pressure's off him, but he's still going to be all business. I can see him there now in his office with a line of guys waiting outside to see him – people downstairs and in front standing around in overalls who never did a day's work in their lives, looking to make sure there ain't any surprise raids. His runners come up to tell him how much each section of the city is doing, how much money he has got laid off, if there's going to be any banana races today, and if there's any big shylock loans coming due. The phone rings and he's got a scrambler on it, but they don't talk. They just say, 'This is the skinny guy. You going to be busy for the next hour?' And Butch says, 'No, come on up.' You see, they have to come in and see him when they want him. And he has a guy come in every week to check the place for bugs.

Anyway, after he's done, he's going to go to dinner, probably at the Amalfi on Fifty-Seventh Street or maybe Gino's. The Amalfi is more likely because tonight's the night the people from Harlem come down. They'll sit at another table, and when he's finished eating, they come over one at a time and say, 'Have you got a minute? I'd like to buy you a drink.' And he sits down and there's no conversation about anything, you know. They talk about the weather. 'How's your mother? Family okay?' In the meantime, the guy puts an envelope in a napkin on the table and pushes it over to Butch, or maybe Butch has to slip one to him. And he sips a little anisette and this goes on maybe until the joint closes at three, four o'clock in the morning. Depends on how much business he has to do. Then he probably heads over to look in on his crap and card games. The biggest one he owns is at that hotel on Seventh Avenue – the place where Anastasia got it in the barber shop. Well, if Butch's going there, he will check in at about three or so and he just goes up and sees if anybody needs a loan okayed, if some guy wants to play and got no cash left. You see, Butch will either say, 'Okay, gives this guy a marker for three.' Or, maybe he says, 'Don't give him anything.' Without Butch, the guy running the game can't take any markers. So Butch stays there until maybe four and then he goes back to where he's staying or he sees a girl.

Now, how do I hit this guy when he isn't surrounded by guys who know me or who are going to get in the way? I'm thinking on this one when the cab rolls up to the front of the motel and I get out and go in the office. The place is empty and I get a room and feel like the guy is looking at me funny because I don't have no car. Now who would stay in a joint like this with no car and no broad? It's not exactly in the middle of things, and I'm beginning to get the feeling I should have done this in Jersey and not right here in Butch's home territory. You know, this part of New York is just all garages, diners, parking lots, and outfits that trade in vending machines, jukeboxes, and pinballs. This is real mobland here. But I know that and I figured coming here was the last place they'd expect me to be. Anyway, I get in the room and lock the door and open the package. What I want to do is saw this shotgun down so it will fit under my raincoat without showing. I got to cut the barrels down to eight, ten inches or so, and most of the stock comes off too. I wind up with a gun that's only a little more than a foot long.

The only trouble about sawing off a shotgun is that it makes a hell of a noise when I'm sawing fast and if I go slow it's going to take all night. So I cover the damn thing with towels and sit on the bed and try to saw holding the gun on my knees. It takes forever. Been so long since I done this I forgot how long it takes. It's real hard steel. And the last time, I had a vise to hold it in, and I did it in a safe place, where I don't have to worry about noise. I'm sawing away and – knock-knock-knock on the door. I stop, open the gun and slip a pair of shells into it and close it quiet, throw a towel over it, and yell, 'Who's there?' The door opens with a key and I raise the gun and the door stops at the chain.

'Maid!'

'What do you want?'

'Just checking if the room's occupied, sir.' And she closes the door and I hear her knocking next door. Maybe it was the maid and maybe not. They don't have any lady marshals or I'd think it was another one of Mister Oakes's people trying to stop me from getting to Butch.

234

So, maybe half an hour later, I finish sawing the barrels off. There's now less than ten inches from where you put shells in to the end where the shot comes out. Now I change blades and start sawing the stock off a couple inches back of the trigger. This is also very slow, since a hacksaw is not made to saw wood, but at least it's quiet. Anyway, I finally get through and the stub of a stock is rough and too short to hold onto so I wrap it with black rubber tape until I can get a real grip. Now the ends of the barrels where they been sawed are very rough and I want to make them smoother, so I wrap the gun in a towel and go out to the parking lot in back and there's no one there, so I get between two cars and rub the cut ends on the cement.

Back in the room, the only thing I got left to do is see if this cannon works. Now, I can't go blasting away even in this rat trap, so I take a couple of shells out — the birdshot — and unload them. I pry the cardboard plug out of the top, dump the shot, and use a knifeblade to pull the wads and then dump the powder. Now I got two shells with nothing live in them but the primers. I slip them into the gun, close it, and pull the trigger — pop! It sounds like a kid's capgun. I open it and the left barrel fired. Close it up again and pull the trigger — pop! — and I open her up. That's the way she's set: pull the first time the left barrel goes, second time the right barrel. Of course, I'll be yanking it so fast it'll sound like one big bang. Now, I wipe the sawed-off pieces of barrel and the leftover stock for prints and roll them up in a couple of sheets of newspaper with all the sawdust and other crap and put tape around the package. I'm all set and I figure I'll go and check out Butch's office and see if I can get lucky.

I put the shotgun in a paper bag and go out through a back door to the parking lot. The package of junk goes in the garbage can there and I flag down a cab out in front. If I can get to him, I blast Butch right now, but chances are it's not going to be so easy and I'll have to come back later, maybe even tomorrow – or maybe whack him some other place. Anyway, I tell the cabbie to go over to Eleventh Avenue and drive downtown slow and I'll tell him where and I'm not in a hurry and I want to think something out and I duke him a couple. You know, tipping ahead is the greatest way in the world to get what you want. Guy's usually worried how much you're going to give him and, bang, you give before he does anything and he can't believe it and figures you might duke him again, so he breaks his ass. This guy's driving me like I was the Pope in the Easter Parade. Thing is, I want to check the garage without asking him to slow down, you know. I don't want him or anyone hanging around to see what I'm up to.

So, we get down to Thirty-Third and Eleventh and I tell the guy I want to go over to a place on the East Side and he should turn across Thirty-Second Street. I happen to know it's a two-way street and only a block long, which is why Butch has his office there. The guy turns on to Thirty-Second and there's not much traffic and I'm thinking this cab stands out like a sore thumb. There's a few trucks and tractor trailers parked in the block, and the garage is about halfway over to Tenth on the north side of the street. I been in the place a hundred times and it looks no different from the outside – an old, beat-up yellow-brick garage over two stories high that takes up maybe a quarter of the block. There's a green metal sign over the main door saying New Holland Garage. Anyway, most of the place is one big open bay with skylights and there's three other big doors with those overhead rollers that come down to close them up. Well, we're passing it now and I can see one lookout for sure, a guy leaning against the wall outside having himself a smoke. There's guys inside, some of them wearing coveralls, and there's a truck up on a lift and another one parked next to it.

236

Now I can see the second-story windows and the fire escape. You see, Butch had the windows upstairs covered over a long time back so from the outside it always looks dark up there, and you can't ever tell if he's in there or not unless you seen him go in and not come out. And he was going to fix a way to get out the back and I'm wondering if he ever did that. If Butch has got a back door, then you can't ever tell if he's there.

Now we're at the end of the street and turning, and I know what the problem is. There's too many guys around for me to get inside and up to Butch unless I can get them away from where they're supposed to be. We do it all the time in setting up a big score – get the cops or the private guards away from where the action is going to be. And the best way to do it is with a bomb. A big one will pull anybody away from anything. If it was big enough and close enough, it'll even get a guy out of bed with his *goumara*. Now, I know how to make a bomb. You can make one from lots of things. You don't need dynamite. A couple of small propane tanks are just as good, maybe better, because they start a fire, too. I'm not going to have the time or the stuff to make a big blast, so fire is the answer. In a garage with all that oil and gas around, it's better anyway. So I tell the driver to make a few more crazy turns and then I want to go back to my motel.

What I'm going to make is an old-fashioned firebomb – a wine bottle full of gasolene and oil and a rag in the top. You light it and throw it and, wham, you got yourself a fire in a hurry. So I'm back in the room and I figure I got to make the thing from what I can find right here in this joint. And I light up a cigarette and sit down for a minute and think on just what's got to be around here. A bottle is the easy part. There's a bar and a kitchen and the garbage out back has got to have plenty of bottles. Rags are also no problem – I got sheets, the towels, the curtains. The hard part is the gasoline. I could buy it

237

or steal it from a car. Can't go to that gas station a few blocks down without a car unless I con the guy that I run out of gas down the road and then he wonders why I don't want his towtruck. Hardware stores are all closed now. The easy way is to rip off a car in the parking lot out back, siphon the gas tank and cut the oil line or whatever. A mess but easy.

But, I'm thinking, you can make a firebomb out of other things, like cleaning fluid or lighter fluid or alcohol or that gummy stuff you put on charcoal before you throw the steaks on. Now none of this is what a professional torch would use on a job. It'd be too dangerous and easy to spot. I mean you burn down a joint with a bottle of charcoal lighter and the insurance company knows from ten miles away it's no accident. They can smell it. But for what I want – something to get the attention of those guys in the coveralls – it's perfect. It'll go off like a bomb and I'm thinking that you don't just use gasoline, you use a mix of gas and oil or gas and soap or rubber glue. Burns hotter and longer. You know, the professionals like to use stuff that's kept around the place they're going to burn, like if it's a bar maybe they use alcohol or if it's a factory they use paint thinner and rubber, whatever. Some of those guys have their own private formulas, a certain stuff that burns like hell but don't leave no evidence and makes it like the fire was an accident.

So I take a walk down the hall and poke in the garbage next to the Coke machine and find an empty whiskey bottle. I throw it back and go outside behind the kitchen and there's a whole can full of bottles, all kinds. Right there in the middle is the one I want, a Chianti bottle with the straw around it. I pull it out and see another one down further and pull that one too. Back in the room I strip the straw off one of them. If you never done that, it looks like a big green light bulb; you can't stand it up without the straw on the bottom. Anyway, this thing will hold a

lot and throw nice, and just to make sure it smashes good
I take my pinkie ring, the one with the three-carat dia-
mond, and use it on the bottle, make scratches up and
down and around. Now I got to put the rag in the top –
and I'm thinking, screw the rag, that's easy. Let's go find
ourselves some firemaker. I walk down the hall and into
the dining room and it's almost empty. Business must be
lousy, or maybe it's too early, except that out-of-towners
all eat early. So I don't see any waitresses and I go back
to the kitchen door and look through the peephole there.
There's a cook messing at the stove and a waitress sitting
down over by the chopping block. I push my way through
the doors and ask, 'When do you close?' I'm giving the
place a fast check while the cook tells me he's short of
help and closing at nine o'clock. I tell him to forget it and
I go back through the dining room and out. Well, the
kitchen has one thing I could use and that's a case of
Sterno in cans – you know that pink jelly stuff they light
up when the waiter makes a fancy dish at your table?
If I could get a half a dozen cans of that and put it in a
bottle I'd have myself a firebomb. Not bad, I'm thinking,
except that the handyman here probably has even better
stuff. You see, the handyman of a joint like this has got to
have paint thinner, floor wax, cleaning fluid, a propane
torch, and all kinds of stuff that burns. The question is,
where is the goddamn room where he keeps his tools and
junk? I'm looking around and I come to a door with no
number on it where the hall goes into the lobby and it's
locked. It could be the workshop or just a storeroom. The
door is heavy and solid and I go outside and I can feel
myself getting frantic. I got to calm down and stop thinking about how this could take all night and even then I
might not be able to come up with a good bomb. The
best thing is to go back to the kitchen and slip the guy a
few for some of that Sterno and whatever else he's got
around there. I know there's other stuff, maybe in the

closets that the maids use, but I don't have time to look for it and I can't go around breaking and entering. I don't want to go out in this neighborhood either. I might be spotted. And the funny thing is that around here is almost as good as the Brooklyn piers for getting anything in the explosive line. I could have ordered a hand grenade or a case of them. I could have got an Air Force firebomb. I could have got anything around here once, but I can't now.

So I go back to the kitchen, but this time I come through the back door. I head outside and through the parking lot to the place where the garbage cans are and sure enough, there's a cook's helper dumping crap out of a bucket into one of the cans. I follow him back into the kitchen and the cook's over there talking on a wall phone and having himself a beer. So I walk over and tap him on the shoulder. He turns, nods, and pretty soon hangs up. I put a folded ten in his hand, and 'Listen, friend, I need some of your canned heat.' And I'm pointing to the case of Sterno. 'About half a dozen cans—' I start to tell him and he's already down on the floor pulling cans out of the box and piling them up on the floor. He puts seven or eight cans on the counter top and rolls them in a piece of newspaper, and, without him saying how much, I duke him another five and tell him, 'I need some gasoline for my camp stove—' The cook nods and trots out the door and three minutes later he's back with a red plastic jug with a pouring spout, the kind you use to carry gas for an outboard motor. And I give him another five and walk out the way I come in. I don't know what the son-of-a-bitch thinks I want with all this and I don't care. I know he says nothing to nobody cause he just made himself a fast twenty selling motel supplies.

Back in the room, I put the chain on the door and lock myself in the bathroom. I don't want to be disturbed for a while and I don't want the smell to get out, so I turn on the little fan they have working when the shower is on. I take the plastic ice bucket and fill it half with gasoline. Then, I open a Sterno can and scoop the jelly out with a spoon and into the gas. It spreads around and melts. Another can the same way and another and another. In ten minutes I get nearly a full bucket of gooey pink stuff that smells like it's going to explode if I breathe hard. So I take a spoonful and drop it in the sink and take the bucket and put it on the floor outside, close the door, and throw a match at the sink and, whoosh, it catches fire and burns like hell, sputtering with the water drops and burning anyway and smelling up the place. It's going to be great.

Filling the bottles and stuffing pieces of towel into the tops takes me another ten minutes. Very messy job, since the bottles won't stand up and the gasoline jelly runs all over the place. By the time they're full I got a headache from the smell. I flush what's left down the toilet and wipe out the sink and bucket. And just to make sure I don't drop these beautiful bombs when I'm winding up to throw them, I put a turn of rubber tape around the middle of each one, something for my fingers to hang onto.

Now I'm ready. A pair of big, green bombs for my old friend's friends, and two loaded shotgun barrels for his face. Not just his face, his mouth. He's going to get it right in the mouth and I want to hear him beg for mercy.

I put the Army coat on, slip the shotgun in my right pocket and five extra shells in my left. I'm only going to use two on Butch but I might have to do a little blasting on the way to him or on the way out. I was going to carry the bombs in the coat, but they make such big bumps that I'd be spotted for something a mile away. You don't have to know what's wrong with a guy to spot him; all you need to know is that he don't look right. So I'm going to carry the bombs wrapped in towels in the shopping bag I got at that hardware store. It's perfect.

241

With the Army coat on, I look a little like a bum or a guy that's out of work. Nobody'd wear a coat like this that didn't have to. And the shopping bag's okay, too. You know, they call them 'Polish suitcases'. So, I double-check everything. Make sure the gun is loaded, my lighter works, I got extra matches in a couple pockets and – that's it. I go out the side door again and get a cab. This time I want to go to Eleventh Avenue and Thirty-Third Street. I pay the guy off and start walking south, wondering if the driver could smell the stuff and feeling like a kami-kaze with the two bombs and a gun. I got enough on me to start a small war over there. And I'm trying to re-member to shuffle along and look like a bum or a cripple here.

It's only another half a block before I turn left and then only a hundred yards and I'm there, and right now I'm wondering if these things are going to go better if I throw them like a quarterback or like a pitcher on a softball team – you know, over or underhand. I figure under is best, like I'll have more control and take less chances of dropping the damn things.

Well, anyway, I'm at the corner now and I cross over to the other side of the street and turn towards Tenth and the New Holland Garage. I'm walking slow now and it's lit up. Stands out on this dark block. There's a couple of street lights down a ways, but the warehouse next to the garage is dark. The building on my side is all closed up. Very little traffic. And I can see even from this far, that there's still a lookout there. Probably not the same one as before, but still a lookout. So I'm maybe fifty yards away from the garage and I stop behind a parked truck and think it over. What place do I throw from? Do I run into the street to get close? What do I do if I miss and the thing hits the outside wall? What if the damn bombs don't go off? What if one goes off in my hand? What if Butch ain't there after all this? Now that's the real question. What if the son-of-a-bitch has changed his schedule or he's sick in bed or whatever? Maybe I should have called him from the motel. I know his goddamn private number, but calling would have been dumb. He'd know it was me and be ready, or anyone close enough to answer the phone would be some guy I know. I can't call the garage number.

I look around the truck here and I'm beginning to feel like someone might be watching me, you know? A guy standing here at night doing nothing, not even drinking out of a bottle or taking a leak, is going to attract attention. Even the cops'd roust me. And I'm looking and wondering if there's really only one lookout, if maybe there's other guys in the dark windows and doors behind me or up on the roof over there. I can only see the one guy, but that don't prove Butch don't have them spotted around. If he does, they already got me in their sights and it does me no good at all to run. I just got to go ahead and make my move, and now.

So I start walking again and I still don't know what I'm going to do except heave these things in that open door and hope I hit a truck. Or even better, I hope I get one under a truck because then there's going to be a big boom and all this commotion so that I can get to Butch without his guards being around.

Now I'm getting near the garage. I pass another parked truck and then one more and I'm twenty, thirty feet from being right across the street from the door that's open, and I'm passing this last truck now and I put a cigarette in my mouth so I have a reason for stopping. I put the bag down and get ready to light up and I can hear a truck coming down the street behind me moving slow. I turn and it's about a five-ton job with a body like a small moving van. And it's stopping and, son-of-a-bitch, turning right into the door of Butch's garage. The lookout is on his feet ... talking to the driver and he slaps the truck's door and the engine roars and the truck is moving. It's going very slow so as not to hit the top on the garage door and the lookout is yelling at the driver and trying to steer him. And I pick up one of the Chianti bottles and put it on the curb so it's leaning against the front wheel of the truck I'm behind. Out comes the other bottle. I light my cigarette and take a deep drag and the truck is through the door now and the lookout is still yelling at somebody inside and I touch the lighter to the rags on top of the bottle and swing my good arm back like I'm in a bowling alley and step up to the line and heave the fucking thing. It goes sailing through the air very slow like a heavy football and – goddamn! – it lands right under the rear of the truck that just went in there and a sheet of flame spreads across the door.

I don't even see where the lookout is now. I light the second bottle and walk out in the street and throw it as hard as I can right into the fire and past the truck I already hit. I hope it goes off in the middle of the floor, but I can't see through all the smoke and fire and I'm not going to try to find out.

There's a lot of noise in there and I wonder if maybe somebody's going to try and peg a shot in my direction. Anyway, I got to move fast, get upstairs and meet Butch as he's coming out. He's not going to jump at the first yell of fire. You see, I figure he's either on the phone or talking across the desk to some guy when the fire starts. Right away he hears about it, but he's not going to panic. Wouldn't look right. He'll finish his business and walk down the hall and take a look, and then – when he sees that the joint is really burning up – he'll duck out the fire-door and take off. At least that's what I think he'll do. And I'm walking away from the fire now, away from the open door and down towards the end of the garage. Down there is where the fire escape is and it ends in one of those iron ladders that are up off the street unless you're climbing on it – the kind that your weight can pull down. Well, the ladder is right over me now, about two feet above my head and if I jump a little I can reach it and pull the damn thing down. And I do. A little jump, like in a kid's basketball game, and I got the bottom rung and the ladder rattles down to the cement at my feet. I make sure the gun is safe in my pocket and climb up to the landing.

Across and up one flight I see a metal door that I know is only ten feet or so from Butch's office. I stand, gun in hand, at the end of the platform, you know, behind the metal door and – wham! – down below there's an explosion in the garage and I can feel the building shake. One of them trucks must have gone up, or maybe it's the gas pump that's right inside the door. Anyway, I'm standing there wondering if Butch is inside and if he is, will he come out this way or come out at all. A couple minutes go by and I'm feeling pretty sure that if he's in there he will come out this way because he ain't going to go down into that flaming inferno and – the door in the wall opens a crack. And then very slow it opens more and a guy steps out careful and starts to walk to the stairs and go down and, soft and clear I say, 'Hold it! Stop right there!' And the guy turns and – it's him. It's Butch.

Suddenly, I know I been holding my breath since the door started to move and I let it out now. I got this son-of-a-bitch in range, got the drop on him. I can put him away and maybe get out of here before anybody knows a damn thing. He's a dead man. No one can save him now. He could come up with a gun in both hands and I'd still blast him to bits before he pulls the trigger. I open the firedoor. I look and see nobody and I motion Butch back inside. We're going to his office to have a little talk and Butch's walking in front of me looking like he always did. Behind me, I think I hear a siren. It's probably a firetruck, but I don't give a damn. They're not going to get up here in time to save this bastard. Butch stops in front of his office door and turns and says, 'I got to unlock it, you know.'

'Move your hand down slow and let me see nothing but keys when it comes up,' I tell him, pointing the gun at him. He's moving in slow motion and I'm getting a funny feeling about him, the way he's acting. I'm not sure what it is, but I learned a long time ago you live longer if you pay attention when something's bugging you. A minute later, the door is open and I'm following him in maybe two feet behind and I lean forward and smash him in the side of the head with my gun a couple times and he goes down. He's not out, but he's gone enough for me to feel for his gun and take it and lock the door behind me. I know no one else has a key to this place. Butch wouldn't trust anybody else to have one. The bastard is beginning to move now and there's a little blood on his ear and I back away towards the door and he sits up shaking his head and calls me a cocksucker and a motherfucking son-of-a-bitch. And he gets to his feet and he's holding the side of his head with one hand and he's looking at me funny, you know, not blazing mad like I'd expected from Butch when he's hurt, and I'm trying to figure what he's got in mind, what he's going to do – try and rush me, talk me out of it, whatever. And he starts, 'You're not going to get away with this, you know. You're going to get hurt. You better give it up now—'

'Listen, you fuck!' I'm yelling at him. 'Shut your mouth! You killed my Nancy!' I can't believe it. The son-of-a-bitch is as arrogant as ever. He's acting like he got the drop on me and I can feel my anger warming up.

'I was always smarter than you,' he's grinning at me. 'How do you think I got where I am? I'm not on the run. You are. Give yourself half an hour's running start and get out of town. I'll do that for you for old friendship.'

246

'Why you little punk!' I'm yelling and I'm thinking if I went for that crap I'd be dead before I got to the door. And I move towards him and he's moving back to his desk. He's probably got another gun there but I don't care because he's never going to get a chance to use it. I got to get myself simmered down or I'm going to do something dumb and blow it all.

'You think you're so damn smart. If you'd just kept quiet we could have had this whole – why did you drop a dime on me?' I didn't plan to ask him that. It just came out.

And he says, 'I put you away. Sure, I put you away, John. I'd do it again. You done things to keep me away from the boss.'

'We could have had New York in the palm of our hands,' I'm saying. 'We could have had it all, you know? How much longer do you think the Old Man could have lived? We were his people. He loved us.' And I yell again, 'You're so smart, you're stupid!'

'You had no right keeping me from the boss,' Butch is whining at me like a kid. He's built up all this hate for years. 'But you did. Why'd you do it to me?'

'I never kept you from anybody.'

'You always had it so easy. The Old Man liked you and you could get away with anything.' Butch is screaming at me. 'I took all the chances. I did the dirty work. And you, you fuck, you got the pat on the back.'

'Listen, you bastard! I was the one that got you in. If I told Don Mario once, I told him a dozen times what a good job you done.'

Butch is almost talking to himself now, 'I was good enough when he wanted somebody hit,' he says, 'but not good enough to get invited out to the house.'

'What do you think, you put it over on these people?' I'm almost feeling sorry for Butch right now. 'They know what you are. They could see right through you that you're crazy. They don't want crazy people around, you damn fool.'

'I'm not crazy! You're the one that's crazy. And you're going to find out. You bought it, Johnny! You're a dead man!' And he starts laughing at me and I'm over to him in one big step and the shotgun is in my left hand and I smash him as hard as I can in the face with my right. I want to drop the gun and beat him to a bloody pulp, but this ain't a movie and I'm not John Wayne so I just hit him again and smash him in the side of the head with the gun. And he's down on his knees and I stick the gun in his face and scream, 'Beg! You son-of-a-bitch! Beg for your fucking life!' And he spits at me and I push the barrels of the shotgun right into his lips. If he says anything they go into his mouth.

And suddenly I know what's been bothering me since I got here. The cocker wasn't surprised to see me. He was not surprised. Which means he's probably got an ace in the hole, only maybe the fire has screwed it up. If anyone was coming to his rescue they're a little late. Anyway, I got the gun to his face, but I'm also trying to get my back away from the door just in case one of his boys has a key, and I'm a little upset that this bastard is so cool that he can be down there on the floor with a shotgun staring him in the face and he's not flinching. I'm wondering and I still can't figure it. And my finger is tightening on the trigger and I'm squeezing slow and my jaw is tight waiting for the blast and I stop. This is too easy. I want this bastard to hurt before he dies. I reach into my coat for the knife and press the button and it clicks open and I take the shotgun out of his face and move the blade back and forth in front of Butch's eyes and he's watching it like it was a snake and I'm going to slash his face so he has a bigger smile than now and then work on a few other places and — wham! I turn fast with the gun, but not fast enough. The door is open and there's Mister Oakes

248

with a piece in his two hands pointed right at my head. He smiles and says, 'Okay, Johnny. Drop it!' So, I drop it.

'Kick it over here!' I kick it over and Oakes picks it up, his eyes never leave my face. Then he lowers his pistol and shoves it back into a belt holster. And I look back at Butch and he's standing up now, smiling like a cat.

'Lock the door, Tom!' says Butch and Mister Oakes turns and locks the door and I'm standing there like a donkey.

'Mister Oakes!' I'm yelling at him and asking with my eyes and I know the answer before he says it.

'I'm sorry, John,' says Oakes, 'but that's the way it is.'

Butch laughs and walks back behind his desk. He opens the drawer and pulls out a revolver. 'You bastard! I'll take care of you now!' And Butch walks around his desk and stops. He makes a come-on gesture and a kissing sound with his lips. His eyes are blazing with hate and he's motioning me over with his gun. 'Okay, Johnny. Down on *your* fucking knees. We'll see how tough you are. You're going to lick my shoes right now!' He's six feet from me and I can't get to him without being blasted, so if I get down on the floor and he comes close I maybe got a chance to grab for his throat and hang on. So, I'm down on my knees and Butch takes a step and then raises his hand like he's trying to stop traffic and – blam! There's a tremendous roar and Butch turns a back flip and lands on the floor. His head is half gone.

I can't believe it. Mister Oakes has just shot Butch Lombardi.

I don't want to believe it. I wanted to kill this fuck myself. I wanted to see him squirm and beg and hear him scream for his life and then when I'd stabbed him and slashed him and kicked him I wanted to hear him ask Jesus and Mary for death and then I wanted to shoot him in the legs and then in the arms and then in the gut and do it one shot at a time, slowly and . . . and, now this rotten, no-good bastard with a badge, this motherfucker has taken my revenge. First he betrays me and then he steals my vengeance. I'm crying and shaking and getting up off the floor. I'm crazy mad. All I can see is Oakes's face in a red haze and I'm running at him. I'll get my revenge anyway. He's not going to cheat me out of Butch. I'll stab him and choke him and cut him and stomp on him and I'll get his throat in my hands and squeeze the life away.

I can see him standing there looking at me and doing nothing. I'm in a slow-motion movie. It's been minutes since I started for him and I'm not there and I feel like someone hit me with a sledge hammer. I'm on my back looking at the little holes in the tiles up there getting red and it feels like I'm sinking to the bottom of a swimming pool. And Oakes is standing over me and holding out his gun.

I can't see him too well, but I know the next one is going to be in the head unless he thinks I'm gone. My eyes are almost closed and I stay that way and I can feel my right hand being moved and my fingers being bent around something. I'm almost out of it now but I can feel my finger on the trigger of the sawed-off shotgun. The son-of-a-bitch is setting things up. A sharp pain, like a cigarette on the back of my hand and I move it and Oakes's voice from far away, 'I figured you might still be here and you know, John, I can't leave you around to tell lies about me.' I look up and I can see his finger squeezing the trigger and his face is dim and out of focus and I know it won't hurt cause he won't miss. And then, there's a noise like a shot, but I don't feel nothing except the floor is shaking and the room is full of people pushing and shoving. Voices. 'Che-rist! Butch Lombardi got it!' and 'Whadda ya know?' And Oakes's voice, 'You see, Captain, I been tailing Forza and I caught up with him about an hour back. Saw him firebomb the place, lost him, then caught up just as they blasted each other.' The other guy mumbles something I can't hear and Oakes's voice again, 'Right, Captain! It's no loss to society. That's for sure.'

WASHINGTON—Senator Samuel O. Harrison (R. Pa.), chairman of the Senate Select Committee on Organized Crime, announced today that John Forza, self-confessed Mafia member turned government witness, was interviewed before his death last Friday in New York City's Bellevue Hospital. Forza, who had recently been a fugitive, was wounded in a shoot-out at the Manhattan headquarters of one of his former underworld associates several days earlier. Senator Harrison said that the material contained in nearly seventeen hours of tapes will result in a number of important organized crime indictments. The tapes have been turned over to the Attorney General. The senator refused comment on reports that the tapes implicate certain high-ranking federal law enforcement officers.

## THE WORLD'S GREATEST THRILLER WRITERS – NOW IN GRANADA PAPERBACKS

### Robert Ludlum

| | | |
|---|---|---|
| The Gemini Contenders | 95p | ☐ |
| The Rhinemann Exchange | £1.00 | ☐ |
| The Matlock Paper | 85p | ☐ |
| The Osterman Weekend | 85p | ☐ |
| The Scarlatti Inheritance | 95p | ☐ |
| Ludlum Super-Thrillers Gift Set | £3.95 | ☐ |

### Ian Fleming

| | | |
|---|---|---|
| Dr No | 85p | ☐ |
| From Russia, with Love | 85p | ☐ |
| Diamonds are Forever | 85p | ☐ |
| On Her Majesty's Secret Service | 85p | ☐ |
| Goldfinger | 85p | ☐ |
| You Only Live Twice | 75p | ☐ |
| Live and Let Die | 75p | ☐ |
| The Man with the Golden Gun | 75p | ☐ |

### Alan Williams

| | | |
|---|---|---|
| Shah-Mak | 75p | ☐ |
| Gentleman Traitor | 60p | ☐ |
| The Beria Papers | 75p | ☐ |
| Barbouze | 85p | ☐ |
| Long Run South | 85p | ☐ |
| Snake Water | 85p | ☐ |
| The Purity League | 85p | ☐ |
| The Tale of the Lazy Dog | 85p | ☐ |

### Gerald A Browne

| | | |
|---|---|---|
| Slide | 75p | ☐ |
| 11 Harrowhouse | 75p | ☐ |
| Hazard | 75p | ☐ |

### Trevanian

| | | |
|---|---|---|
| The Loo Sanction | 95p | ☐ |
| The Eiger Sanction | 85p | ☐ |

# THE WORLD'S GREATEST THRILLER WRITERS –
## NOW AVAILABLE IN GRANADA PAPERBACKS

**Len Deighton**

| | | |
|---|---|---|
| Yesterday's Spy | 60p | ☐ |
| Spy Story | 75p | ☐ |
| Horse Under Water | 85p | ☐ |
| Billion Dollar Brain | 85p | ☐ |
| The Ipcress File | 85p | ☐ |
| An Expensive Place to Die | 85p | ☐ |
| Declarations of War | 60p | ☐ |
| The Best of Len Deighton Gift Set | £4.25 | ☐ |

**Peter Van Greenaway**

| | | |
|---|---|---|
| Doppelganger | 60p | ☐ |
| The Medusa Touch | 85p | ☐ |
| Take the War to Washington | 75p | ☐ |
| Judas! | 75p | ☐ |

**Ted Allbeury**

| | | |
|---|---|---|
| Snowball | 50p | ☐ |
| A Choice of Enemies | 60p | ☐ |
| Palomino Blonde | 50p | ☐ |
| The Special Collection | 60p | ☐ |
| The Only Good German | 75p | ☐ |

**Robert Rosenblum**

| | | |
|---|---|---|
| The Sweetheart Deal | 65p | ☐ |
| The Good Thief | 75p | ☐ |

## TRUE CRIME – NOW AVAILABLE IN PANTHER BOOKS

**Ludovic Kennedy**

| | | |
|---|---:|---|
| A Presumption of Innocence | £1.25 | ☐ |
| 10 Rillington Place | 95p | ☐ |

**Stephen Knight**

| | | |
|---|---:|---|
| Jack the Ripper: The Final Solution | £1.25 | ☐ |

**Peter Maas**

| | | |
|---|---:|---|
| The Valachi Papers | 75p | ☐ |

**John Pearson**

| | | |
|---|---:|---|
| The Profession of Violence | 95p | ☐ |

**Ed Sanders**

| | | |
|---|---:|---|
| The Family | 95p | ☐ |

**Vincent Teresa**

| | | |
|---|---:|---|
| My Life in the Mafia | 95p | ☐ |

**Colin Wilson**

| | | |
|---|---:|---|
| Order of Assassins | 95p | ☐ |
| The Killer | 60p | ☐ |